Praise for Marlene and *Go Vegan*

Scientific research shows when delicious filling foods, such as those found in *Go Vegan*, are an available option, then compliance to a healing diet is phenomenal – 85% of people will adhere to a low-fat vegan diet for at least one year. Why not? The food tastes great and you can eat as much as you want, while at the same time losing your excess body fat and regaining your attractiveness and health. Marlene Watson-Tara's life changing book will help you along this journey.

John McDougall, *MD, physician, author, and educator*

Marlene Watson-Tara's *Go Vegan* provides you with everything you need to transform your health! From her great recipes, key nutrient information, and personal testimony, you will leave feeling inspired and ready to get started.

Neal D. Barnard, *MD, FACC, author, clinical researcher and founding president of the Physicians Committee for Responsible Medicine*

It is obvious that Marlene Watson-Tara wants us, her readers, to be healthy and happy while enjoying great-tasting food. In *Go Vegan*, Marlene gifts us with bright, clear explanations of the why???s and how???s of plant-only cuisine, and then expertly presents dozens of mouth-watering recipes that brings this luscious, animal-friendly, Earth-healing cuisine to life. The fabulous photos are sure to motivate you to try these dishes yourself, and, who knows, you may be the first among your friends and family to *Go Vegan*. I assure you, after tasting the delicious dishes in this delightful book, you'll be glad you did.

Dr Michael Klaper, *physician, author, educator, Moving Medicine Forward*

Marlene Watson-Tara is, without any doubt, the world's leading authority on macrobiotic vegan nutrition and, with her partner, Bill Tara, is a pioneer of the modern natural health movement. She is literally a walking encyclopedia of information about health and nutrition and has a passion to share it with everyone. And, like all of those with a true passion, Marlene does what she does not because she is seeking fame or fortune, but because she cares so very deeply about others – human and nonhuman alike – and about the planet we all inhabit. In this book, Marlene provides vegan recipes that will not only please your taste buds but that will nourish every cell in your body and help you to achieve maximum health. *Go Vegan* is far more than a book of magnificent recipes. It is a book that explains the theory of healthy eating in an accessible and engaging way, and that will change the way you think about food forever.

Gary Francione *and* **Anna Charlton**,
professors of law and of human and animal rights

This is an amazing book! So full of information presented in such a readable format as to be understood and enjoyed by all, especially sensitive to those who are transitioning to a healthier lifestyle! As for myself, admitting to not being of a chef's mentality and capability I was seduced by the simplicity of the recipes and the organisation which made it so easy to find exactly what was desired for the occasion!! Thank you, Marlene! You are a genius!!!

Dr Martha Cotrell, *physician, activist, teacher*

Marlene is the embodiment of character and competence. In my 39 years in the health industry I have never met anyone more congruent and knowledgeable on the fundamentals of good health. Marlene's passion is informed by a lifetime commitment to the science of nutrition, health, healing and human ecology. Her commitment to excellence is evidenced by the content of this book and her passion comes alive with a beautiful pictorial display of her mouth-watering recipes. She communicates the joy of veganism and its importance to our health as individuals and as a planet. As you delve into this beautiful book you will become as big a fan as I am.

Dr Steven Cangiano, *assistant professor of surgery
at the New York College of Podiatric Medicine,
wellness director at the Metropolitan Wellness Group
in New York and publisher of* Humanity Upgrade Magazine

Go Vegan is *the* book I will constantly have on my book shelf. Also, this book should be on the book shelves of everyone who wants to see the change in not only their lives but in the world. Marlene's *Go Vegan* Cookbook has elevated Vegan Cooking to new heights!!

Mayumi Nishimura, *author of* Mayumi's Kitchen *and private chef to Madonna*

There are vegan cookbooks and then there's this vegan cookbook. I often say that anyone can cook vegan food with refined ingredients like white flour and white sugar. The real challenge ... and triumph comes with cooking from whole ingredients to create luscious foods that serve the purpose of your life. With *Go Vegan*, Marlene has done exactly that. Taking cooking past the how into the realm of why we cook, she offers insights into the impact of food on wellness. A must-have book for anyone who loves food ... so pretty much everyone.

Christina Pirello, *Emmy-Award-winning host of* Christina Cooks, *bestselling author*

In *Go-Vegan*, Marlene Watson-Tara offers a compelling and comprehensive work that broadens the vegan template with mouth-watering, visually stunning photographs and nutritionally balanced fare. For kitchen new-bees, it'll guide you with easy-to-follow instructions that showcase a new culinary world of tastes and textures; while experienced cooks will discover healthy, imaginative and inspiring recipes organised with succinct clarity. Toward the back of the book she includes smart and savvy nutritional information. Warning: This book will make you WANT to cook!

Verne Varona, *author of* Nature's Cancer-Fighting Foods

What could be better than delicious food? Delicious food that's going to improve your health with every bite! That's what *Go Vegan* is all about. Marlene has been teaching health for decades. With this book you will receive the very best of all her recipes and knowledge spanning all those years.

Dr Nandita Shah, *recipient of the prestigious Nari Shakti Award 2016, the highest award for women in India, for her pioneering work in the field of health and nutrition; author of* Reversing Diabetes in 21 Days

Marlene Watson-Tara's passion for healthy food, the welfare of all sentient beings, and the future of the planet is contagious! In *Go Vegan*, she introduces a practical, dynamic, and satisfying way to transition to a wholesome, plant-rich diet that will increase your health and vitality, benefit creatures great and small, and help sustain the earth as a whole.

Alex Jack, *president of Planetary Health, Inc., co-host of the* Miso Happy Show, *and co-author of* The One Peaceful World Cookbook

There is such joy in Marlene's cooking, you feel happier just eating her food. Her recipes are always delicious and beautifully presented. She shares her wisdom and knowledge in this book that entices us back to our kitchen. She quite rightly states that cooking has become a lost art world-wide and her book perfectly captures what's happening in today's 'food world'. This book is more than a cookbook. It is life changing filled with wisdom that only Marlene knows how to convey. The world is ready for *Go Vegan* with our dear Marlene.

Princess Béatrice d'Orléans Paris *and* **Madrid**

I've known Marlene for many years, and we have shared unforgettable moments. She is a person I truly love and admire for her intelligence and who always makes me laugh with her sense of humour. She is active, positive and never gives up on her vision. I would say more than anything, Marlene is a force of nature. *Go Vegan* is yet another of her fantastic contributions in the world of Macrobiotics and Vegan healthy living.

Thank you for existing and contributing to make the world a wonderful place for us all to live in dear Marlene.

Geninha Horta Varatojo, *author,*
founder of the Instituto Macrobiotico de Portugal

Our modern world is in desperate need of healing, of body and soul, in need of nurturing ourselves, our families, our society, and our planet. Where do we start? Where can we deepen our knowledge of foods, cooking, and consciousness? Marlene Watson-Tara's new book *Go Vegan!* is one of the best tools to begin, to submerge, to indulge in delicious wholefood, natural vegan meals to generously satisfy our senses, our philosophy, and our body. A true mind-body-soul education is here in this book. It is time for the world to awaken to Marlene's nutritious, satisfying, and scrumptious meals, that bring freshness, color, and fun to the family table once again.

Do not fear. Marlene is like a warm, friendly companion who comes into our kitchen to begin the magic and art of cooking … cooking to create healing and joy. *Go Vegan* is absolutely amazing and a must for everyone who is vegan or aspires to eat consciously, ecologically, humanely … and deliciously. The gorgeous and enticing photographs of her creations inspire us to be more healthful, creative, and ethical … yes, let us put our philosophy where our mouths are … eating conscious foods. This is the true genius of Marlene and this treasure of a book. It is the perfect book to share with loved ones who are just beginning to tiptoe into veganism.

Marlene's writings reflect knowledge that is clear, powerful, and motivating. Passionate about health and nutrition as a Scottish youth, Marlene is equally passionate about animals and living humanely on the Earth. Connect with her energy, savour her knowledge, cook with her, learn macrobiotic wholefood vegan classics with her special pizzazz! Let her be the Sherpa up the mountain, for she has truly climbed high up, accompanied by her equally amazing husband, Bill Tara. We can only thank her for her sharing her spirit, her knowledge, and her book, *Go Vegan*. As her father taught her, Marlene is speaking and sharing the truth.

Lino *and* **Jane Stanchich**, *Great Life Global, USA*

Go Vegan

A guide to delicious, everyday food – for the health of your family and the planet

MARLENE WATSON-TARA

Your expert in healthy vegan living

'Certified good health'
'This book deserves to be on the shelves of all connoisseurs and chefs of good food. Enjoy!'

T. Colin Campbell, author of *The China Study*

lotus
publishing

Chichester, England

First published in 2019 by
Lotus Publishing
Apple Tree Cottage, Inlands Road, Nutbourne, Chichester, PO18 8RJ

Photographs Helen Cawte
Cover Photograph Alex Stanhope
Cover Design Alissa Dinallo
Text Design Medlar Publishing Solutions Pvt Ltd., India
Printed and Bound in India by Replika Press

British Library Cataloging-in-Publication Data
A CIP record for this book is available from the British Library
ISBN 978 1 913088 03 3

To my 93-years-young superstar mum, Mary Watson, whose message is:

It's never too late to change – go vegan

(Mum became a fully fledged vegan on her 90th birthday)

and

to my late dad, John Watson, who taught us seven kids:

Always use your voice to speak the truth

The doctor of the future will no longer treat the human frame with drugs, but rather will cure and prevent disease with nutrition.
Thomas Edison

Contents

Foreword *by T. Colin Campbell* 13
My Mission and Vision 14
Acknowledgements 15
Welcome 16

The Ecological Kitchen 21
Food Texture and the Five Tastes 25
Conquer Your Kitchen 29
Four Weeks to Vegan – the Transition Made Easy! 37
Kitchen Equipment 39

What's for Breakfast? 43
Marlene's Mighty Bowl of Goodness Brown Rice Breakfast Porridge with Toppings 44
Dried Berry Granola 48
Tofu Scramble 51
Sweet or Savoury Buckwheat Crepes 52

Sumptuous Soups 55
Quick Miso Broth 56
Summer Sweetcorn Chowder 59
Roasted Squash and Sweet Potato Bisque with Ume Plum and Almond Cream 60
Black Bean Soup with Sour Cream and Chives 63
Adzuki Bean Soup with Tamari and Ginger 64
Tarragon-Scented Parsnip Soup with Sourdough Croutons 67
White Bean Soup with Almond Pistou 68
Spicy Brown Lentil Soup with Sour Cream 71
Chickpea and Vegetable Soup with Crunchy Peanut Butter and Walnut Croutons 72
Creamy Mushroom Soup with Savoury Cashew Cream 74

Quick Bites 77
Grilled Portobello and Roasted Red Pepper Sandwich 78
Mediterranean Chickpea Salad Sandwich 81
Vegan Bean Burritos 82
Vegan California (Uramaki-Style) Sushi Roll with Ginger-Tamari Dipping Sauce 85
Crispy Sweet and Sour Tempeh Sourdough Sandwich 86

Big Bowls 89
Three Bean Chilli Bowl 90
Rice and Corn Fusilli with Broccoli and Lemon Cashew Sauce 93
Yakisoba Bowl 94
Millet Sesame-Crusted Tempeh Veggie Bowl with Sweet Peanut Sauce 97
Vegetable Seitan Rice Bowl 98
Lemon-Infused Baked Tofu Brown Rice Bowl 101
Ramen Bowl with Fresh Daikon and Greens 102

Global-Fusion Main Events 105
Red Lentil Coconut Curry 106
Almond Mung Bean Burgers with Sweet French Fries 108
Old-School Macro Plate 111
Lasagne 114
Sourdough Pizza 117
Cornbread, Greens and Beans 121
Barley Risotto with Shiitake and Sweet White Miso 124
Marlene's Vegan Paella 127
Sizzling JaJa Tofu 128
Vegetable Pad Thai in Tamarind Sauce 131
Rice and Bean Enchiladas 132
Teriyaki Black Bean Burgers 135
Portobello Mushroom Stroganoff 138
Saffron-Scented Vegetable Tagine on a Bed of Herbed Couscous 140
Vegetable and Tempeh Wellington with Shiitake Gravy 143
Roasted Red Pepper and Chickpea Korma 146
Tricolour Quinoa and Vegetable Stir-Fry with Teriyaki Sauce 149
Spaghetti with Basil and Watercress Pesto 152
Vegan Shepherd's Pie with Shiitake Gravy 155

Lip-Smacking Sides and Salads 157
Creamy Coleslaw 158
American Noodle Salad 161
Couscous Rainbow Salad with Lemon and Lime Tahini Sauce 162
Cucumber Wakame and Peach Salad with Ume Tangy Sauce 165
Nishime Vegetable Stew 166
Nest of Steamed Kale with Pressed Salad and Sweet Vinaigrette 169
Asparagus with Vegan Hollandaise Sauce 170
Lemon-Scented Arame Sauté with Toasted Walnuts 173
Ginger-Glazed Carrots and Watercress 174

Roasted Vegetable Combo. 177
Herb-Crusted Baked Cauliflower. 178
Crispy Potato Wedges with Ketchup 181

Delish and Divine Sauces, Dressings and Dips. 183

Ketchup 185
Sour Cream. 185
Classic Hummus 186
Salsa 187
Guacamole 188
Thai Dressing. 189
Basil and Watercress Pesto 191
Lemon and Lime Tahini Sauce 191
Marlene's Rich Tomato Sauce 192
Rich Shiitake Gravy 193
Oil-Free Mayonnaise 194

Sweet Nosh. 195

Gingered Apple Sauce with Cashew Cream and Crunchy Granola 196
Mum's Black and White Chocolate Cake. 199
Peach Kanten with Sweet Date Cream 200
Chocolate Adzuki Bites 203
Sweet Cherry Ice Cream with Chocolate Sauce 204
Oatmeal Walnut Cookies. 207
Lemon Tart. 208
Mini Orange Chocolate Pots 211
The Sweet Nosh Bar. 212
Choc Chip and Raisin Cookies 215
Carrot Cake with Lemon Frosting 216

Teas and Macrobiotic Home Remedies 219

Immune Booster – Magic Mineral Broth 221
Digestive Aid – Ume Sho Kuzu. 223
Kidney Tonic – Adzuki Bean Tea 224
Chlorophyll Tea – Parsley and Coriander Drink 224
Fat Buster – Dried Shiitake and Dried Daikon 225

The Human Ecology Diet: *Nutrition for the Future, by Bill Tara* 226

Human Health 229
Environment 231

Economy 232
Social Justice 232
Regard for All Life 233

What We Eat: *Organic, Seasonal and Local when Possible* 234
Whole Grains 235
Beans. 238
Vegetables 242
Fruit 245
Nuts and Seeds 246
A Japanese miscellany. 247
What about Nutrition? 253

Resources 261
Index 263
About the Author 272

Foreword

Marlene Watson-Tara has been an unusually dedicated woman in the cause of furthering human welfare through eating food that matters. Her tradition, and that of her husband Bill, is drawn from their long-time association with the famous macrobiotic diet concept introduced in the West by Michio and Aveline Kushi during the 1950s.

The Kushis spent their entire lives advocating for good health. As a result, their collection of papers and books on macrobiotics and alternative health care were entered as a permanent collection at the Smithsonian Institution's National Museum of American History. I was honoured to be the featured speaker at that 1999 ceremony, while Michio Kushi spoke to my class at Cornell University.

Marlene has collected for this book a number of really scrumptious recipes based on her own teachings and travels – the pictures alone make my mouth salivate – and I am confident that they are as healthy as they are appealing to the eye. No added fat, right combinations of whole colourful plants, and certified good health.

This book deserves to be on the shelves of all connoisseurs and chefs of good food. Enjoy!

T. Colin Campbell
Co-author of *The China Study* and *Whole*
Professor emeritus of nutritional biochemistry
Cornell University, Ithaca, NY

My Mission and Vision

My wish is that you embark upon living this way of life and approach it with excitement. We are not driven by the latest food fad or popular theory, but on a solid principled approach that takes into account modern science, ancient wisdom and human ecology.

Bill and I have been very fortunate over these past decades to have developed the gift of knowing how to take good care of ourselves and others in terms of food and lifestyle. It's our passion and pleasure to share this way of living with all who cross our path. Our services are based on our combined experience, spanning over 90 years, working as health consultants, authors and teachers. We love to empower our students and clients to create a healthy way of living by learning the life skills that we have seen consistently work to improve health.

Join us in service for a healthy world for humans and non-humans alike. Thank you.

Acknowledgements

My heartfelt gratitude to Lotus Publishing for presenting me with the opportunity to create this cookbook. I am indebted to my copy-editor, Maia Vaswani, for her keen editorial eye and guidance, along with her good cheer. Huge thanks to Dom Hoile for his wonderfully creative styling of my recipes, and to Helen Cawte for her stunning photography.

I wish to present my special thanks to Richard Murray and Mary Jane Higgins for their belief in my work. Richard has been a very special friend to this project from day one. I have endless appreciation and much love for him for assisting my work to grow worldwide.

I would like to express deepest gratitude to my mum and dad, Mary and John Watson, for teaching me at a young age to never give up on what vision we hold dear in our hearts. Thank you to my amazing superstar siblings – Jacky, Marguerite, Sandie, Shirley and Elaine – who are without a doubt my biggest cheerleaders. All of them such special souls. They have listened to me forever rambling on with passion about my vision for a vegan world.

Love and gratitude to my best friend, love of my life, my inspiration and husband, as well as chief editor, Bill Tara. I owe him much. Bill's patience is like no other's, his continued praise or critique delivered with a sense of humour as he read through my work was priceless. He lets me do what I do best: talk! I write with increased excitement as my ideas appear on screen. Without Bill's editing, my book would have been the size of the *Encyclopaedia Britannica*, and that was only the first chapter.

I would like to pay special thankfulness, warmth and appreciation to all of my students and clients around the world who constantly support my work. And to my fellow vegans who use their voices to raise the awareness that all animals are sentient beings and treasure their lives just as much as we do – I hug you all. Being vegan is not a sacrifice, it is one of the great joys of life. Let's continue to educate and change the world. It's a world worth saving. I honour each and every one of you who promotes veganism as a moral imperative.

Bill and I visualise that 2019 will be the year that we all unite to become strong and unapologetic change-makers. Non-violent vegan education is key. It is great fun teaching and helping others; it's what brings us the greatest joy.

In good health

Marlene X

Welcome

A warm welcome to our Human Ecology Diet.

I have written this book for many reasons, all of which are driving forces in my daily life. They are health, food, our planet and my love of animals. All of these are at the heart of everything I do.

Since I was old enough to remember, my love of food and cooking has brought me the greatest joy. I became interested in food at a very young age. I grew up in Glasgow, Scotland, and pleaded with the local fruit and vegetable shop to let me work there. He wouldn't hire me until I was twelve years old because I wasn't tall enough to reach all the shelves. I loved to work there among the grains, beans and vegetables. I guess my future was already making itself known to me.

Like many people, my early experience of sickness drew me to discovering all I could about health. I suffered huge health setbacks in my teens. Those experiences inspired me to find out on my own about being healthy. I was the lone teenager joining Glasgow's first health club, 'The Olympic', at the age of fifteen, and discovered seaweed as a dietary supplement. My studies on anatomy began in that first health club, and I became a part-time personal trainer (alongside my day job) and later commenced studying yoga, t'ai chi and traditional Chinese medicine. All my studies pointed to the fact that food was the key to health.

Food brings people together. Food should taste great, provide us with optimal health and satisfy our appetite. I do believe that food can be our best medicine, hence my unfailing desire to teach everyone who crosses my path that health and healing truly start in your own kitchen.

My passion is to demonstrate that making delicious and nourishing healthy food is achievable. I find it exciting to create new recipes and train chefs and home cooks utilising my seasonal menus and cooking skills, incorporating the five tastes and my understanding of macrobiotics.

Changing your diet always means finding replacements for less healthy options. I want to share with you healthier and tastier alternatives to whatever you desire.

You will find these recipes are easy and affordable. In fact, all our clients tell us that they have saved upward of 60% on their food bills since eating our Human Ecology Diet.

In my previous book, *Macrobiotics for All Seasons*, I categorised the recipes according to seasonal eating. The book was focused specifically on the macrobiotic way of balancing food; this book is different. Here I have used a broader range of tastes. This is for those people who want a healthy vegan approach without sacrificing taste. These are dishes to convert the doubters. My students from around the world will testify to that.

The recipes vary from quick meals for busy people to elegant dinners for guests, and my wish is that you find the book a valuable resource to bring health, healing and environmental sensibility back into the kitchen. Simply pick and choose from the recipes in each category. There is ample choice that can work well for everyone.

I use an array of plant foods that are whole and natural and prepared with just the right mix of condiments, fresh and dried herbs, and mild spices to create robust, satisfying delicious flavours.

I don't consider this food to be a 'diet'. This is simply healthy, tasty cooking. It gives all of us the advantage of creating a harmonious relationship with our environment whilst ending the suffering of the animal kingdom – an important focus in my four decades of teaching. As a long-time healthy vegan, my work brings me the greatest joy, and to share this message with as many people as I can is my life's mission.

The ideas that drive the vegan approach to living are not new. For the centuries since the times of Pythagoras, thousands of thoughtful people have questioned the use of animals for food. Those concerns have usually been moral considerations about killing sentient life, but concerns for health and our relationship with nature have been considered as well. As winner of the Nobel Prize Albert Einstein said, "Nothing will benefit human health and increase chances of survival for life on earth as much as the evolution of a vegetarian diet." That evolution has arrived, and it is veganism.

Famous people who stopped eating animals include Leonardo da Vinci, Leo Tolstoy, and two other Nobel Prize winners – George Bernard Shaw and Isaac Bashevis Singer. You don't have to be a Nobel Prize winner to get the message. In present times the sensibility of a vegan diet has spread out into the arts and athletics. The number of professional athletes who have switched to a vegan approach to eating include swimmers, skiers, weightlifters and those in team sports, and include multiple modern Olympians. There is rumour that the word 'vegan' comes from the Latin word *vegetus*, meaning 'strength of mind and body'. Who really knows? Based on the evidence, it sounds right to me.

My Mentors

No one lives in a vacuum. We are all influenced by our experiences, our study and by the people we meet.

The following eight people have been my inspiration – all of them wise and trusted teachers who speak the truth. I could in fact write a book about each of their accomplishments alone. They share intellectual curiosity, enormous energy, perseverance and the ability to see the connections between things.

Let me start with the 'Scottish connection' – Dr. Dennis Burkitt, who gave me a huge light-bulb moment about dietary fibre. As a young Scottish lass, a mere teenager and constantly constipated, my doctor told me I had a lazy bowel and would have to take laxatives for the rest of my life, or my appendix would burst. I refused to take the medicine and, consequently, guess what? My appendix burst and nearly killed me with peritonitis. I survived, all the wiser but wanting to know why the condition was there to begin with.

Much to the amusement of my friends I took to the library to start learning about diet and health, and I have never stopped learning over these past forty-five years.

Dennis Burkitt was a surgeon and physician – the 'Fibreman' who observed the role of dietary fibre while working in Africa. He was also a distinguished researcher and identified Burkitt's Lymphoma. 'The only way we are going to reduce disease', he said, 'is to go backward to the diets and lifestyles of our ancestors'. Dr Burkitt's explanation of why I was sick sparked my interest in studying human ecology.

T. Colin Campbell is the Jacob Gould Schurman Professor Emeritus of Nutritional Biochemistry at Cornell University and the co-author of *The China Study*, the most comprehensive study of nutrition ever conducted. Professor Campbell's research and writing have had the most important single influence on bringing the issues of dietary reform into the public eye. His promotion of a wholefoods plant-based diet added much-needed credibility to the food revolution. He is an inspiration.

John McDougall is the author of *The Starch Solution*. A physician and nutrition expert who teaches better health through 'It's the Food', he has been studying, writing and speaking out about the effects of nutrition on disease for over fifty years. He is the founder and director of the internationally renowned McDougall Program. Dr McDougall has been one of the trailblazers of the movement away from an animal-based diet, and an outspoken critic of nutritional nonsense for decades. He is the man of truth.

Gary L. Francione is the Distinguished Professor of Law and Nicholas deB. Katzenbach Scholar of Law and Philosophy at Rutgers University School of Law. He is an author and leader of animal-rights law and ethical theory, and the abolitionist theory of animal rights. Professor Francione's advocacy for animals has inspired thousands of vegans to move beyond superficial quick fixes and into the heart of our relationship with non-human life. A revolution of the heart.

Anna E. Charlton is an adjunct professor of law who, along with her partner, Gary Francione, founded and operated the Rutgers Animal Rights Law Clinic from 1990 to 2000, making Rutgers the first university in the United States to have animal-rights law as part of the regular academic curriculum. Anna co-authored *Animal Rights: The Abolitionist Approach* and *Eat Like You Care* with Professor Francione.

Neal Barnard is a physician, fellow of the American College of Cardiology, clinical researcher, author and an adjunct associate professor of medicine at the George Washington University. He is the founder and president of the Physicians Committee for Responsible Medicine. The work of Dr Barnard has provided important inroads to the orthodox medical community and his is a strong voice in defence of animals.

Michael Klaper, known affectionately worldwide as Dr K, is a gifted clinician, internationally recognised teacher, and sought-after speaker on diet and health. As a source of inspiration advocating plant-based diets and the end of animal cruelty worldwide, Dr Klaper contributed to the making of two PBS television programs: *Food for Thought* and the award-winning movie *Diet for a New America* (based on the book of the same name). Dr Klaper teaches that 'health comes from healthy living', and he is dedicated to the healing and flourishing of all living beings and our planet.

Bill Tara has since 1967 been an active advocate for natural healthcare and macrobiotics. He was a pioneer in the natural-health movement in the 1960s in both America and Europe. His educational work includes being the founder of the Community Health Foundation in London, and co-founder of the Kushi Institute for Macrobiotic Studies in the 1970s. Bill has been invited to over twenty countries to speak on macrobiotic philosophy, health and environmental issues. (Another accomplishment is that he is my husband!)

All of these incredible and dedicated teachers have written numerous books and articles. I have listed their 'classics' at the back of this book in the 'Resources' section, along with their website details. Their work will change your life forever.

The topic of nutrition has become a bewildering landscape of cultural myth and vested interest. There is an urgent need for a new approach to human diet, one that cuts through the commercial PR, the political caution and the nutritional confusion.

The **MACRO**Vegan approach to eating addresses these concerns with a fusion of two important doctrines. The first of these is the ecological insights of ancient Asian healthcare found in macrobiotic studies. This tradition points to the benefits of seasonal, regional and ecologically sustainable nutrition. The second set of standards comes from the ethic of the modern vegan approach to eating that drives the leading edge of contemporary nutritional science, proven by both medical study and extensive epidemiological research.

The **MACRO**Vegan way of eating addresses the requirements for vibrant health as well as a delicious, diverse and socially responsible way of eating, as expressed in our Human Ecology Diet.

I remember reading *The China Study* in 2005 and thinking, yes! The world will now change with this book. We are getting there slowly, but *too* slowly. Please share the work from all of these wonderful humans with family, friends, colleagues and, quite frankly, anyone who has a pulse!

When we are driven by passion and not fear, everything falls into place. When nature is in jeopardy, we MUST take action. All living organisms exist as interconnected parts of the natural whole. No element is superfluous, not even the smallest insect or microbe. This entire system is sustained by natural energy of the elements. With climate change impacting our global environment in so many ways, it seems that nature herself is punishing us for the way we live.

> We often speak of 'producing food' but farmers do not produce the food
> of life. Only nature has the power to produce something from nothing.
> Farmers merely assist nature.
> **Masanobu Fukuoka**

> Education is the most powerful weapon
> which you can use to change the world.
> **Nelson Mandela**

The Ecological Kitchen

No one really knows when humans started cooking their food, but one thing is sure: every culture did it. For over a million years we have been learning the magic of food and fire. It doesn't matter if you live in the frozen north or the jungles of the tropics, human beings cook their foods.

Our ancestors discovered that cooking makes food easier to digest, brings out hidden flavours and kills off harmful bacteria. It is a basic life skill and is now more important than ever. As food processing becomes more industrialised, the use of chemicals in the growing, transport and processing has increased. Food has lost much of its nutritional value and is laced with mystery ingredients. It's time to reclaim the kitchen and know what we're eating. Making our own food in our own kitchen is creative, empowering and heathy.

As a graduate of T. Colin Campbell's Cornell course in plant-based nutrition, I can assure you that these recipes not only please the senses but are designed to improve personal and planetary health. There is no reason why the foods that are proven to contribute most profoundly to our health cannot be prepared to provide delicious meals. We should expect it.

When nutritionists attend our Macrobiotic Health Coach programme, they tell us that we have opened a huge window of opportunity for them. Instead of merely offering their clients supplements, they start to teach them how to cook. That's what makes me excited. Getting people back into their kitchens.

You will find morsels of information throughout the book in sidebars. They are identified by these symbols:

The microscope **indicates science**
When you see this sign there will be a short note of recent science that confirms the health benefits of a vegan diet. You may be surprised that most of this information has been available for decades. It is heartening that a message that presents such hope and potential to both prevent and manage disease is finally filtering into the mainstream. Veganism is not a fad; it is an important movement towards redefining good nutrition and having an ethical approach to eating.

The tree **indicates the environment**
This icon represents the environment. For many people the shift to vegan eating is driven by environmental concerns. One of the most important aspects of our food choices is the impact that they have on the planet. It is a fact that some of the most critical influences on climate change and species loss are directly related to what we eat. A healthy diet should be sustainable and benefit all life, human and non-human alike.

The spiral **is ancient wisdom**
The thoughts and actions you will find under this symbol we call ancient wisdom. We have a tendency to think that 'modern' is always best, but this is not always the case. Our collective ancestors prized some traditions that are especially important for living a healthy life. Some of these had to do with food selection or preparation, and some addressed our way of thinking. Remember, *there is nothing new under the sun*.

It's not difficult to be vegan
In our combined ninety years' teaching, Bill and I have high hopes we can all come together and make a better world, a healthy **vegan world** where humans and non-humans alike live in harmony. Success can only be achieved through education, understanding and, ultimately, action. Let's face it, back in the time of Copernicus, most would have thought it impossible if you said that you were going to convince everyone that the Earth revolved

around the Sun, rather than the other way around, but it did eventually happen! So, the past teaches us to have hope for the future.

Going vegan is simply a choice you make. Many people waste a lot of energy pondering this as if it were a complex issue, but the only difficulty lies in making the decision – it's easy. Remove all the animal-sourced foods and replace with delicious plant-based foods – the choice is yours. You can do it right now. It may take you a while to locate your best food sources and become comfortable with your new way of eating, but it's worth it.

When we reflect deeply on our relationship with the outer world, our environment, we realise that we are never independent of its influences. Food is the link between the inside and the outside world. Our Human Ecology Diet is abundant in every vitamin and mineral required for good health, vitality and longevity.

Rethinking protein

Protein is a subject that always comes up when discussing veganism. When you think of the biggest animals on the planet – elephants, giraffes, buffalo – these are huge mammals; they don't eat meat, so where do they get their protein? They eat what grows out of the ground and that is where they get their protein; it's as simple as that. We have all been sold a mythology that only animals have protein, without asking where they got it from.

Plants are the source of all protein. There are many foods in the plant kingdom that are especially rich in protein. All the legume family – anything that grows in a pod, lentils, beans and chickpeas – and whole grains are full of protein, and many vegetables are rich in protein too.

Plants are high-energy foods, and it's good to note that an increasing number of athletes are switching to a vegan diet. Recent winners of long-distance events like triathlons, marathons and bicycle events are eating a vegan diet. These athletes recognise that they get injured less often, recover more quickly and have more stamina when they eat a diverse plant-based diet.

Many years ago, I was listening to a webinar by Dr John McDougall and it reminded me of some of the things I learned as a twelve-year-old working at the veg, fruit, grain and bean shop. Here I am fifty years later, having so many of these same lessons gaining notice. It is mentors such as Dr McDougall, Dr Barnard and T. Colin Campbell who brought these simple truths to light again. Here are just some of these gems:

- Vegetables are easy to grow – any gardener can grow potatoes, carrots, greens, etc. – and they are inexpensive; rice and beans are also inexpensive (especially when you buy in bulk).

- Animal meat is not required to build muscle or bone. This is a myth that is based on limited and biased science generated by the livestock and dairy industries.
- Plants are lower on the food chain, so the environmental pollutants that are so prevalent in our food are in lower concentrations in plant-based foods. Animals are fed food grown with pesticides, herbicides and chemical fertilisers, and drinking water exposed to industrial pollution. These contaminants are stored in the fatty tissue (including the milk) of the animal. They can concentrate 1,000-fold as they go up the food chain. This concentration of toxic products affects all animals on land or at sea.
- Plants are environmentally friendly. You can grow 17 times more nutritional energy on a piece of land if you grow vegetables than you can if you raise animals for food. The difference between growing potatoes and raising beef is 100-fold.
- We are all living on a planet that is food-stressed. There is a real risk of food shortages and security. We need to grow more healthy food. There are close to one billion people (our brothers and sisters) starving to death, while nearly one billion people are eating themselves to death.
- 85% of non-communicable diseases are related to the modern high-fat, high-calorie diet that is low in nutritional density.
- Vegetables don't grow microbes that are pathogenic to people. They don't grow *E. coli*; they don't grow mad cow disease; they don't grow listeria. If a vegetable or grain does have a contaminant on it, then it originated from an animal. Animal faeces are a major agricultural pollutant.
- Vegetables taste amazing. Sweet potatoes, fresh corn on the cob, rice, and so on, are full of natural sugars and a broad range of taste without any added sauces.
- Vegetables store well – you can dry and store rice, beans and grains in a cool place for years. Tubers, roots and cabbages can last months and retain their nutritional vitality.
- Wholefoods (not processed junk food) are great foods for weight loss. Remember, they are low in fats.
- Everything that breathes wants to live – killing animals for our pleasure must stop. Please GO VEGAN and love all of life is my message, and has been for decades.

Making the change

Don't make a shift to a healthy vegan diet be a trauma (or a drama). You are already eating vegetables, grains, fruits and maybe even beans in your diet. You are simply removing the animal-sourced foods and the simple sugar. Your body will thank you. The key is diversity.

People around you may be amused or even sceptical about your new choices. Don't worry – when they see that it can be done, and that you are happy with the results, they will become more interested (or not). Don't expect everyone to support you; simply stick to your plan. Some people recommend that slowly introducing the new way of eating is the best. Everyone has to choose their approach for themselves, but our experience is different.

We always suggest that our clients and students make a commitment to adhere to their new eating plan for at least a three-week period to start. There are practical reasons for this.

As you change your diet you will find that your tastes change. When you remove some of the foods you are used to you may miss them for a short time – but remember your reasons for change. You will find that your new way of cooking opens up a different appreciation of plant-based foods. We call this period 'creating a new normal', and making veganism the new normal is my mission, so stay with me on this.

Changing our food habits is usually an eye-opening experience. How you feel, your energy levels and your food satisfaction will all improve. When you feel great on your new approach to eating why would you want to change? Simply make sure that your food is tasty, and your meals include a diversity of grains, beans and vegetables. The recipes you find in the following chapters will serve you well. I use an array of plant foods that are whole and natural and prepared with just the right mix of condiments, fresh and dried herbs, and mild spices to create robust, satisfying and delicious flavours.

Food Texture and the Five Tastes

As a long-time proponent of a wholefoods, plant-based diet and a health counsellor within the principles of macrobiotics, I adore the whole concept of energy in nature, called 'chi' in traditional Chinese medicine. It is a way of understanding the rhythm and patterns that exist in the natural world. This study is usually referred to as the 'five transformations', and is one of the foundations of this ancient form of understanding health and healing. It makes so much sense to me. Part of the study is applied directly to cooking by understanding the **five tastes**.

The five tastes are one reason that so many people love Chinese food – the tradition lives on. Each taste is thought to stimulate a specific organ system and represents a particular season of the year (five seasons in the system). In cooking we try to get a balance between tastes and make sure that a meal is not dominated by one taste only. It may only be by adding a condiment or a garnish, but when a range of tastes are experienced, we become more satisfied.

The five tastes are **bitter, salty, sweet, sour** and **pungent**. A food will never contain one exclusive taste; there will always be a variety of tastes. Here are some examples of food sources and the connection to the organ for each taste. It is said that a little of a particular taste can strengthen an organ system, whereas an excess can weaken it. Hence, too much sugar weakens our soil energy and stomach/spleen/pancreas, and contributes to digestive problems.

Bitter – Associated with the early and midsummer season (**fire**). Bitter foods are thought to stimulate the heart and small intestine. These foods include dandelion, parsley leaves, mustard greens, collard greens, burdock root, sesame seeds, cereal-grain coffee substitute and some types of corn. This taste is often used in garnishes and not in main dishes.

Salty – Associated with the winter season (**water**). Salty food imparts strength and is thought to influence the kidneys and bladder. These foods include sea vegetables, miso, soy sauce, sea salt, umeboshi salt plum and natural brine pickles. The salty taste features in soups and sauces, not as a table condiment.

Sweet – Associated with the late summer season (**earth**). Sweet food is thought to influence the pancreas, spleen and stomach – organs of sugar absorption and distribution. Its nourishing effect is stabilising and relaxing. The sweet taste refers to natural wholefoods and not the excessively refined sugars and sweeteners that are common. Sweet foods make up the largest percentage of our meals. These foods include whole grains and vegetables – especially cabbages, sweet potatoes, carrots, onions, squashes and parsnips – as well as fruits.

Sour – Associated with the spring season (**wood**). Sour-tasting food has a constrictive effect, producing a quickening energy. It is said to influence the liver and gall bladder. These foods include sourdough bread, vinegar, wheat, sauerkraut, pickles, lemon and lime.

Pungent – Associated with the autumn season (**metal**). The pungent taste gives off a hot, dispersing energy and is said to be beneficial to the lungs and colon. Pungent foods have been known to stimulate blood circulation and, according to folk medicine, have a natural ability to help break down accumulation of fats in the body.

Hot, Hot, Hot – What most people refer to as the hot taste isn't a taste at all, it's a sensation. It is not registered on a taste bud but on the surface of the tissue of the mouth. In fact, too much of the hot sensation can blunt the ability to taste more subtle flavours in food. In most culinary traditions, hot flavours are commonly combined with protein-rich foods and with foods high in fat. Hot foods include spring onions, daikon radish (or dried daikon) and ginger. The extremes are jalapeño peppers, wasabi (dry mustard), cayenne pepper and horseradish. Add these in as you like, but you will notice I do not use the extreme heat in my recipes.

Examples of the five tastes

This system reflects not only the taste of the foods but also characteristics of growth and digestion and effects of the food on the body. Biological classifications of foods such as grains, beans, vegetables, nuts, etc., do not apply. For instance, rice is seen as stimulating metal energy and buckwheat as strengthening water energy. This is the same with different varieties of beans. The classifications are more aligned with tastes in the choice of vegetables and condiments.

Some examples in each category are:

Bitter – Kale, collards, mustard greens, parsley, endive, celery, arugula, grain beverage
Salty – Sea salt, tamari, shoyu, miso, sea vegetables, sesame salt, umeboshi plum, pickles
Sweet – Corn, cooked onions, squash, sweet potatoes, yams, cooked grains, cooked cabbage, carrots, parsnips, fruits
Sour – Lemon, lime, sauerkraut, umeboshi plum, fermented dishes, pickles
Pungent – Ginger, garlic, raw onions, white radish, red radish, spring onions, shallots, wasabi, spices.

A note about umami

Recently, a Japanese scientist identified what is being called a 'new taste'. **Umami** is the earth taste of mushrooms, and can be brought out in foods by cooking with kombu sea vegetables.

While most of your meals will contain a minimum of 60% sweet foods (whole grains, vegetables, beans and fruit) you can aim for a full range of other tastes with major meals. Other tastes can be represented in side dishes, sauces and condiments, emphasising a particular taste you may crave. There is a definite art to meal balancing. Meals that include the five tastes will prove more satisfying, in terms of limiting cravings, and more fortifying.

What about texture?

Aside from taste, both smell and texture are important for enjoying our food. The smell factors you will get when you cook your food, but the texture comes into play when the food is eaten. Crispy, chewy, soft, firm, creamy, smooth and crunchy are not the names of the seven dwarfs from Snow White! Food should have a variety of textures as well as tastes.

Baked vegetables such as squash and even carrots can be very soft and smooth to the taste; roasted seeds as a garnish can add a pleasant crunch to a meal. Creamy sauces and gravies complement chewy whole grains nicely. A nice sourdough pizza crust or a seared tempeh dish can add a lovely crispy taste. Play around with your meals and consider the texture of them – you may be surprised at the way a variety of textures brings out new appreciation.

This brings us to another factor in cooking: cutting skills. The way that you cut your vegetables can change the texture of the dish and alter the appearance of any recipe. Keeping this in mind will help you determine what type of cut is appropriate for the dish you are cooking. I usually use larger cuts of vegetables in stews, roast vegetables and winter dishes, and smaller dice and thinner cuts in light salads and soups. A smaller cut results in a sweeter soup, as the sugars from the vegetables are released into the broth. The thickness of the cut affects the cooking time as well. If you are dicing a variety of vegetables, remember that the denser ones will require longer cooking time.

Conquer Your Kitchen

Here are some of my top tips to make your kitchen work for you. The kitchen cupboard is the nerve centre of your kitchen – keep it well stocked and you will save time dashing to the shops for that single ingredient, and will always have a delicious meal at hand even when the fridge is looking bare.

Tasty dressings

You can make delicious sauces and dressings and wonderful-tasting dips using all-natural ingredients that incorporate the five tastes. Toasted sesame tahini, umeboshi plums, brown rice syrup and barley malt, shoyu, sweet white miso, fresh ginger juice, lemon juice, and tofu, the possibilities are endless. All of these delicious dressings can be used on salads, boiled vegetables, noodles or pasta, and sea vegetables. Many of them can be stored in the fridge for up to five days.

Quick bites and roll-overs – cook once, eat twice

Time savers are a great way to cook your food. Cook double and use the rest for tomorrow's lunch. Cook more than you need and freeze the rest. A good idea is to freeze in small portions, so you have 'ready-made' meals when time is of the essence.

- Make a weekly menu plan – it makes it possible to use leftovers efficiently and makes meal preparation simpler.
- Make double the sauce and use for another dish later in the week.
- Salad dressings are easy to prepare in larger batches. Depending on the dressing, it will keep for at least a week, although some can be stored for a month or longer. Dressings are versatile and can be used not only on salads but to also dress up simple vegetable and grain dishes and add a quick boost of flavour.
- Cut enough fresh vegetables for several days and store in an airtight container so that all the cutting is done and you can cook quickly.
- Peel and chop carrots, onions, etc., bag them and freeze. When needed, just take out as much as you require and reseal. Not perfect, but helpful.
- Mince fresh garlic and keep it in the refrigerator for ready use. Minced garlic will keep for about two weeks in the refrigerator in a sealed container.
- Juice several fresh lemons or limes at a time and store the unused juice in the refrigerator in a sealed container. This will save time when putting together salads, dressings and other recipes. Fresh lemon juice will keep for about ten days.
- Beans will last three days in the refrigerator after being cooked. Cook enough beans to use in a soup, stew or casserole. I cook up batches of adzuki beans and freeze them in portions.

- Grains will last up to five days in a sealed glass container in the refrigerator. I make our short-grain brown rice porridge for breakfast in one batch that lasts us through the working week. I simply warm the required amount each morning for breakfast by adding some water (you could use a rice milk). Grains and beans are good to reuse with a nut or seed garnish, but make the vegetables fresh.
- Prepare larger amounts of brown rice, beans and other longer-cooking foods and freeze them in small portions so they will defrost more quickly when you need them and will be the right amount required for the number of people you are serving.
- Learn how to use a pressure cooker, crockpot or slow cooker. Pressure cooking can cut standard cooking times by about two-thirds, while preserving more nutrients than conventional cooking methods.
- Purchase some good organic soup stock cubes. I use umami instant stock sachets that instantly deliver a delicious base for all my soups, stews, risottos, pies and even stroganoffs.
- Sea-vegetable dishes last for days. Cook up a good amount and then use a small portion every other day. I switch between, arame, hijiki and nori.
- Always have some wholegrain pasta (brown rice pasta is good), bulgur, couscous and other partially refined grains at hand for last-minute meals.
- Have a stock of shop-bought organic cooked beans and other foods on hand for when you get stuck.
- Choose two new recipes from your cookbooks every week so that you are constantly expanding you range of dishes and your familiarity with the foods.
- Adding some raw vegetables or sprouts to each meal is a winner and it's simple as no cooking is required!

Replacements

There are some foods commonly used in cooking that we avoid for health or ethical reasons. You can be creative and use replacements that will give you the tasty results you expect. Most of them have to do with recreating the 'mouth feel' of another food. You will be pleasantly surprised with your results.

Replacing eggs

    1 egg = ¼ cup puréed pumpkin
    1 egg = ¼ cup puréed prunes
    1 egg = ½ mashed banana
    1 egg = ¼ cup silken tofu, blended

Replacing fats and oils

    1 cup oil = ½ cup apple sauce or pumpkin purée
    1 cup butter = ¾ cup pumpkin purée

Replacing milk
Oat milk
Soy milk
Rice milk

Cheese flavours
Nutritional yeast
Nut-based cheese

Replacing sugar
1 cup sugar = 1 cup apple sauce or banana purée
1 cup sugar = ¾ cup puréed dates

Other sweeteners
Fruit purée
Balsamic glaze
Banana purée
Real fruit jam
Fruit preserves
Dried fruits
Barley malt
Rice syrup
Maple syrup

For sautéing use filtered water or vegetable broth, and for roasting vegetables, if you cook them slow at a low temperature they will brown beautifully. I often mist the vegetables I am roasting with a water spritzer and then add some sea salt and my favourite herbs. Always line the roasting pan with parchment paper to avoid the vegetables sticking. For deep frying there are many alternatives, an air fryer being one of them – crispy foods but without the artery-clogging oils.

Short cuts to healthy eating for busy people!
Many people think you are tied to the kitchen when you eat this way – not true. If you organise yourself you can spend literally 20 minutes in the kitchen and have a delicious meal ready by having prepped and stored various items like vegetables, grains, and bean dishes and soups beforehand. As you can see from the above quick tips, a breakfast, lunch or dinner can be put together in no time at all. It is all about planning ahead and being organised. Storing and reheating cooked food makes it possible to serve delicious healthy meals in as little as 10 or 20 minutes. Using soba, udon, quick-cooking grains, and lightly boiled or steamed vegetables allow you to cook up something tasty in no time.

Soups are easily frozen – even individual portions. It is as easy to cook a soup or stew for five or six portions as it is for one. If you know you are going to be home late, simply defrost and heat up when you come home. A hearty soup with some sourdough bread makes a great quick dinner.

Breakfast

Here are some quick breakfast tips. Warm some leftover whole grains for a delicious and nourishing breakfast porridge. Add seeds, nuts and dried fruit of your choice. Or toast or steam some sourdough bread and spread it with some apple butter or bean spread – it's delicious! Slice an apple and have a serving of some toasted pumpkin or sunflower seeds with it.

Kukicha twig tea can be made in batches so you only need add some boiling water to it. At the weekends when time is not of the essence, make some tofu scramble and serve with a toasted sourdough baguette, or make some buckwheat crepes or fluffy pancakes with blueberries.

Personally, I always start the day with a small bowl of miso broth to alkalise my body, and then have short-grain brown rice porridge. Most days I also have a serving of steamed greens on the side. We have lived in many countries and my breakfast never changes. I love it and live it and it fires me up for the day. The energy of the complex sugars burns steadily though the day, not simply flaring up and burning out. It is the difference between a log fire and a paper fire.

Lunch

Heat up some leftover soup; make enough soup for two or three days. Steam or sauté leftover grains or make sushi with leftover rice. Any grain like quinoa is a delightful lunch served with a fresh green salad and one of my dressings. Make some hummus, salad greens, sauerkraut sandwiches, the list of delicious lunches you can put together using rollovers is quite incredible. You will find some delicious sandwich recipes in later pages, and the fillings can be stored for days in the refrigerator.

Dinner

Use rollover bean stew or rollover burgers by reheating and serving with some freshly cooked vegetables and a grain or noodle of your choice. Tempeh and tofu also cook up quickly and can be served with a sauce or dressing that you have previously made and stored in the refrigerator. Sautéed greens with fresh shiitake mushrooms take only minutes to cook; serve with leftover whole grains and top with toasted flaked almonds, again using one of the sauces or dressings. This makes a tasty meal with a minimum of effort. Refer to the recipes in this book and start creating your own dishes.

Make one or two of the following to add freshness to your rollovers:

- Blanched vegetables
- Steamed vegetables
- Mixed salad greens
- Sprouts
- Pressed salad.

Once you become familiar with all the ingredients you can whiz up a delicious healthy lunch or dinner for family and friends like a professional chef with the minimum of effort.

There are many readily available ingredients that will also enable you to make a healthy meal quickly, such as tofu, tempeh, vegetable, bean, or grain burgers; natural pesto sauces; sauerkraut; and hummus. However, read the labels as many can be high in added sodium (salt) and sugars.

Cravings can be expected as the body readjusts to new food. The body likes routine and habit, and upsetting that apple cart, even in a positive way, can create cravings for the foods you have chosen to eliminate from your diet. Most of these preferences are simply habits, sometimes with emotions attached, such as for food we ate as a child.

With a little creativity, you can cook to rid yourself of such cravings as your body adapts to your new way of eating. I have written an e-book called *Freedom From Cravings* – it's available for free from our on-line store on our website. I suggest you download it and learn all about dopamine, those little neurotransmitters that can thwart your efforts when changing your diet.

As you get more familiar with the foods you will find tastes, textures and smells that replicate the things you love, and your tastes will change. Once you have adjusted, cravings will play a much smaller role. Just avoid all animal foods, including eggs.

A macrobiotically oriented vegan diet is a beautifully balanced symphony of mostly unprocessed, seasonal foods, prepared in a manner that will nourish you. If the food we eat is chosen from the wide array of choices Mother Nature provides and is prepared deliciously, cravings and binge eating will be a thing of the past. It all begins with a change in thinking.

Stock your kitchen with some basics
- A variety of grains (a full list of grains is at the back of the book)
- A variety of beans, dried
- Jars of organic cooked beans
- Dried sea vegetables

- Barley or brown rice miso
- Sweet white miso
- A variety of noodles and pasta
- Natural sweeteners: all-fruit jams, rice syrup, barley malt, etc.
- Dried fruit
- Seeds and nuts
- Condiments.

For your refrigerator
A colourful array of vegetables for daily use is key to a healthy vegan diet. My fridge is filled with leafy greens, parsley, coriander, spring onions, broccoli, etc., and my vegetable rack stuffed head to toe with plants such as carrots, parsnips, garlic, fresh ginger, lemons, limes, sweet potatoes, squash and cauliflower.

You will save money being a vegan
There is a huge misconception that it is expensive to eat this way. On the contrary, as I mentioned earlier, we hear from so many of our students and clients that they have saved heaps on their groceries since becoming vegan. Depending on where you live in the world, food choices vary, but vegetables, beans and grains are always available.

Eating this way is not an elitist exercise. While some of the recipes in the following chapters are special dishes (the kind of things I might cook for guests), most are simple to make and easy on the purse.

Remember that grains, beans, vegetables, fruits, nuts and seeds form the largest part of your diet. These items can be purchased in bulk for the lowest cost, and generally go a long way. A cup of dry rice will convert to three cups of cooked rice. Beans are a similar value. If you are on a tight budget, simply make the most of the grains, beans and vegetables and you can still make nutritious and tasty meals.

The most expensive items on your shopping list will be condiments, herbs and spices. These items will be used sparingly and only comprise a very small portion of your meal plan. You can build up your condiment section as you go.

Cooking for one
If you only cook for yourself, success comes from planning ahead. A little preparation will save you time and money, and assure that you stick to your desire to eat healthy food. The first step is to follow the set-up discussed above and make sure your shelves are stocked with healthy food, and plan ahead. Clean your cupboards of junk food – if it's there you will eat it! Plan to succeed.

The biggest problem that people have is cooking the same dishes over and over again. When boredom sets in, junk food (even 'healthy' junk food) beckons. Making a couple of sauces or dressings and keeping them for when you are pressed for time is a winner. Remember that most grains and beans can be kept for several days and recycled into stews and soups.

The key is not to spend a whole of a lot of time cooking every day, but to cook some items, which can be used in a variety of ways, in bulk. For example, you can prepare a pot of rich tomato sauce, healthy soup recipes and a pot of rice all at the same time. It takes very little prep time and almost no time attending the stove.

Watching football on Sunday? Perfect time to cook up some meals in advance. Just prepare some slow-cooker recipes! These are easy to prepare, and you can watch the game and not the stove!

The bottom line is – you can be successful in cooking for one. With a little planning you can serve up quick, healthy and cheap meals for yourself. Since you control the ingredients, a healthy home-cooked meal beats unhealthy takeaway food anytime!

Tips for eating healthily while travelling

Whether you're travelling by plane, train, boat or bus, if food is provided on your journey, make sure you state your dietary needs when you make your reservation. My tips for a hassle-free journey and holiday are easy to implement.

Always request what you want – don't be shy. Your needs can either be met or not, but you never know until you ask.

Whether we are hiking, biking, touring or chilling on a beach somewhere, we are always organised with what we desire for eats and drinks. There are some great sandwich and quick-bite recipes later that are perfect for travel food. Preparation is the key.

I find that when I am on a plane and unpack my lunch the people around me always wish they had my lunch rather than the food being served. Finding a smoothie or juice bar, which are in just about every airport, can be helpful. Every year more restaurants carry vegan options, so fill up before your journey.

When visiting a new city, we always have food with us, or have checked ahead for local shops and cafés. Miso soup sachets, oatcakes, rice cakes, some dips, some vegetable sticks, nuts and seeds, nori rolls, etc., and of course some of my tasty treats. We never go hungry; we always plan to succeed. I also take some apples, blueberries or red grapes – simple and very easy to bring with you.

We're all human and we're all creatures of habit. When we get hungry and we need energy, the first thing our brain looks to is something that's a quick fix, like sugar. Most of the time it's not the good sugars that you would find in a piece of fresh fruit, so having some healthy snacks as options is good. If you don't plan ahead the junk starts looking good.

Search out healthy restaurants at your destination and add as much nutritional value to your trip as possible. If you cannot have your usual short-grain brown rice, eat white rice, it's not a deal breaker. Eating out is relatively simple these days. Every Italian restaurant will make you a delicious pasta and vegetable dish. Middle Eastern, Japanese or Mexican restaurants are plentiful, so feast up on rice and beans or vegetable sushi. Salad bars are common. You never need to be stuck finding something healthy.

Four Weeks to Vegan – the Transition Made Easy!

One of the biggest challenges that people face in changing to a healthy way of eating is simply knowing what to eat, and how to make delicious meals for themselves and their families. Where to start gets so many people stuck that I stepped up to the plate, so to speak, and simplified the process. Quite a few people stop eating animal products and start eating loads of processed junk 'vegan' alternatives. So, the question is, 'My fellow vegans, are you eating right?'

My solution – four weeks to vegan

Some people go vegan overnight, others don't. I wondered how could I assist those people in changing to enjoying a life filled with delicious plant-based food and embracing a vegan life. So I created a course many years ago with this title, and have had huge success. Male and female clients of diverse ages have all found success following this plan. The course features a weekly rotation of Saturday classes, each focused on a basic element of cooking. Here is what we do.

Clients learn four breakfasts, four lunches, four dinners and four desserts. Master breakfast and lunch and you are two-thirds of the way there. Many of them go vegan after the first week, which is wonderful to witness. At the end of four weeks the clients have experienced the preparation of sixteen dishes that they can use to start a new way of eating. Their new-found knowledge on plant-based nutrition, as well as their cooking skills, serves them well and it is how they succeed. Bill and I cover a range of topics during lunch. Our model becomes their game plan. It makes my heart sing to switch on more lighthouses around the world.

You can replicate this plan by simply learning several dishes out of the following chapters each week. Remember to learn a good number of the quick meals as well as some of the more time-intensive ones. After several weeks you will have a delicious and healthy rotation of your favourites. Invest a little more time at the beginning to assure success.

I feel it is important that we educate ourselves. If you review the information at the back of the book it is helpful when answering people's questions. Feel confident in your own personal reasons for making these changes in your diet. Make sure your diet is diverse – don't get stuck eating the same things every day.

Be on the lookout for vegan products at your local grocery shops and vegan items in local restaurants. Always read the ingredient lists and ask questions. This can be done without becoming a nuisance. Simply know what you want and ask for it.

There are lots of wonderful documentaries and books to help you on your way. You will also find a list of some great books to help inform you regarding the issues of the vegan way of life. My YouTube site is also listed at the back of the book, featuring many cooking videos with me.

There is a difference between adopting a vegan way of life and going on a diet. Your education will help you to stay focused. If you stay away from animal products and are re-educating your taste buds at the same time, you will be amazed how easy this all is. The ethics of this way of eating outweigh many desires you might have to return to former food habits. Focus on what you are doing, not on what you are not doing. Veganise your favourite meals; you will find examples in the following chapters. Stay positive.

First and foremost is to feel excited about embarking on this new way of living. It seriously is a great joy to know you are not harming another being whilst enjoying delicious food.

If you have been inspired by a documentary or television programme and think you want to go vegan but are not sure, start with breakfast. Once you have that handled, then move on to lunch. When you have mastered the art of vegan living seven days a week for both breakfast and lunch, you are almost there. The next step is to choose your favourite recipes and master meals that you love.

The recipes in this book offer you something from just about every continent. You will be spoiled for choice. Last but not least, we now master our favourite desserts. Within a few weeks you will be amazed at how much lighter you feel, more conscious, almost like a veil has been lifted. Your energy will be soaring, and you'll think, 'Wow, now I have to start educating others.' That's the plan. We are all lighthouses, all of us.

Kitchen Equipment

It may take you time to assemble all the tools for your perfect kitchen, but don't panic. Start with what you have, and get cooking. For busy folks like myself, I learned quickly which tools I needed and which ones I didn't. I always try to purchase the best high quality and versatile kitchen essentials – they give you the most value for your money. It will also make cooking a pleasure. This list of kitchen essentials that I use and recommend below will have you serving up meals like a professional chef in no time.

Chef's knife

If you've only ever used a cheap cutting knife for your cooking needs, switching to a high quality knife is the difference between night and day. When you upgrade to a professional chef's knife, chopping and slicing will become one of your favourite hobbies!

And since you can use a chef's knife for all your cutting needs (and use it every time you cook), one high quality purchase will serve you for years to come. Currently my knife is 18 years old, and I chop and slice 365 days a year.

Paring knife

A paring knife is a kitchen knife with a short blade that can be used for a multitude of tasks. You can peel and chop with it, and the small tip is great for fine work like coring strawberries (or similar). As with my chef's knife, I purchased a top-notch Japanese brand.

Chopping board

One of the most basic tools you need in your kitchen is a good chopping board. You'll be using it every time you cook. Like your chef's knife, it's important to choose one that's durable and well designed. Take a look at the bamboo range. They are superb pieces of equipment, and you are being kinder to the planet by investing in bamboo rather than hardwood.

Measuring cups

Getting the volume of liquid or solid cooking ingredients in a recipe correct can be the difference between a tasty dish and a train wreck. It's not a good idea to simply guess or measure quantities with a cup or a glass you have hanging around in your kitchen. I use a stainless-steel set of cups that are sized for ⅛ to 1 cup.

Measuring spoons

As above, invest in correct measuring spoons, particularly key when baking. The ones I use contain from 1 tablespoon down to ¼ teaspoon. They're magnetic and nested so you can put them away easily without losing any of them (which can often happen for the smaller spoons). They are double-ended, with an oval shape at one end and rounded shape at the other. Ideal for fitting into packets or jars.

Wooden spoon

An important utensil in the kitchen is a good wooden spoon. It's great for stirring and scooping. When it comes to dishes like risotto, a wooden spoon is customary as its texture helps to rough up the grains of rice. My wooden spoon is made of solid beechwood with a natural oil finish. To keep it in top condition, oil regularly and hand wash.

Mixing bowls

I prefer glass bowls that are multipurpose and won't absorb stains and odour. For mixing together grains, beans, vegetables, salad dressings, marinades and sauces, and even for storing leftovers, a set of high quality mixing bowls is a must.

Colander

This is an essential piece of equipment for draining pasta or washing vegetables and salad greens. Please do not purchase plastic colanders, for obvious reasons. My stainless-steel colander is over 20 years old.

Salad spinner

Please wash all your green vegetables and use a salad spinner to dry them. This will prevent your greens from going soggy. The spinner will keep your greens fresh and crisp. I store them in the salad spinner in the fridge.

Grater

Choose multipurpose tools and avoid single-purpose tools whenever possible. Instead of purchasing different types of graters, a zester and a chiffonade, a multipurpose grater will allow you to grate citrus, and fine, coarse and ultra-coarse shave and slice. Many of these multipurpose tools even have a ginger grater. The one I have is made of high quality stainless steel and will last a lifetime.

Garlic press

Thanks to a gift from one of our beloved students, Larry Tadlock from Hawaii, I have the best garlic press on the planet. It is Swiss-made and delivers minced garlic to perfection. But if you don't mind crushing and chopping your own garlic – great.

Locking tongs

For stirring and flipping and turning and tossing, even for plating and placing. A good pair of tongs becomes something like an extension of your own hand. For serving spaghetti and noodles, it is a seamless tool to use in the kitchen.

Citrus juicer

The one I use fits oranges, lemons and limes and makes juicing a joy.

Stainless-steel wok

A stainless-steel wok is the workhorse of my kitchen. For your enjoyment of cooking and to achieve perfect results, it's important to pick a high quality stainless-steel wok with a heavy base, or the ceramic range that is equally durable.

Sauté pan

A sauté pan is different from a frying pan. It has a wide flat bottom and vertical sides that generally go up much higher than a frying pan's flared sides do. This pan also comes with a lid. I use it to make stir-fries or for slow braising tempeh or tofu.

Small saucepan

For small-portion cooking of soups, stews, pastas or sauces, a lightweight and easy to handle saucepan is necessary. Please use a good quality stainless-steel heavy-bottomed saucepan for excellent cooking results. Cheap thin-based pans will cause your food to stick.

Medium saucepan

A medium saucepan is the one that is used most in our kitchen. I use this saucepan for making breakfast porridge, ramen noodles, miso soup and cooking corn on the cob, which I could quite frankly eat to a band playing!

Large pot

For cooking large dishes like soups, bean stews, pastas or large quantities of sauces, you'll need a large pot to handle the volume. A large pot is also perfect for making your own broth and medicinal teas.

Pasta cooker/stockpot

This multipurpose pot allows for steaming, boiling and cooking. With a stockpot base, riveted side handles, a vented and toughened glass lid, and strainer insert, this stockpot can be used for everything. It is perfect for cooking one of my husband's favourite foods – pasta.

Steamer

A simple three-pot steamer is a very helpful item. Quick steaming of vegetables is an efficient way to 'cook simple'. You can steam briefly to retain the crunch but soften the fibre, or cook longer to create cooked vegetables to meet the needs of your dinner.

Pressure cooker

I think a pressure cooker is an absolute essential for cooking grains and beans. You don't require one with all sorts of bells and whistles. Purchase the best quality stainless steel. This pot will become your new best lifetime friend.

The old saying 'you only get what you pay for' rings so true with cooking equipment. Make a wish list and have family and friends buy you some of these items for your birthday or Christmas, or just because they love you.

Slow cooker

A slow cooker, also known as a crockpot, is a countertop electrical cooking appliance used to simmer at a lower temperature than other cooking methods, such as baking, boiling and frying. This facilitates unattended cooking for many hours of dishes that would otherwise be boiled: soups, stews and other dishes (including beverages, desserts and dips). A wide variety of dishes can be prepared in slow cookers.

The recipes I have created for this book are nutritious and delicious for all the family to enjoy. It is these foods that Bill and I use in our daily life and that form the foundation of our courses. I use these foods in my 'ancient foods for modern cooks' workshops, and you can now replicate these dishes in your own kitchen. They will leave you satiated, relaxed and happy. I am excited to have you here.

What's for Breakfast?

Breakfast is the most important meal of the day. Breakfast kick-starts your metabolism, helping you burn calories throughout the day. It also gives you the energy you need to get things done and helps you focus at work or at school. Those are just a few reasons why it's the most important meal of the day. Every morning I gain incredible energy and health from my power-packed breakfast.

- Marlene's Mighty Bowl of Goodness Brown Rice Breakfast Porridge with Toppings
- Dried Berry Granola
- Tofu Scramble on Sourdough
- Sweet or Savoury Buckwheat Crepes

Marlene's Mighty Bowl of Goodness Brown Rice Breakfast Porridge with Toppings

Cooking the rice
In the pressure cooker
Place two cups of rice in a sieve and rinse under cold running water. Put in a bowl and soak the rice overnight. Discard the soaking water and add the rice and 4 cups of filtered water and a pinch of sea salt to a pressure cooker. Close, seal and bring to full pressure. Reduce to a low simmer for 25 minutes. Remove from the heat and allow the pressure to be released naturally, about 25 minutes. Remove the lid, and hey presto! You now have perfectly cooked short-grain brown rice.

In an open pot
Wash and rinse the rice in a sieve. Transfer to a heavy-based pot. Bring rice, pinch of sea salt and 3 cups of filtered water to a boil. Cover, place a flame spreader under the pot, reduce heat to medium low, and simmer for 30–40 minutes, or until all the water is absorbed.

Makes 4–6 servings.

Note – This batch of rice will stay fresh for up to six days in the refrigerator. Double or triple the quantity to make enough for yourself or your family.

Below is the list of ingredients for my mighty bowl of goodness. I add one tablespoon of each of these powerhouse ingredients to my morning rice. The food of warriors for sure.

The Magnificent Seven
Hemp seeds, along with chia seeds, flax seeds and walnuts, are the richest wholefood sources of the omega-3 fatty acid alpha-linolenic acid (ALA). ALA is converted to DHA and EPA, the omega-3s that are crucial for brain health. Hemp seeds also provide plant sterols, iron and vitamin E. The seeds are composed of about 30% fat and 25% protein, and can provide a wholefood, nutrient-rich boost of protein for athletes who may need extra endurance. Hemp seeds are also rich in arginine, an amino acid that helps to keep blood pressure down.

Chia seeds are a wonderful source of fibre (soluble fibre in particular), calcium and magnesium. Inflammation and oxidative stress will drop when used daily in one's diet. These tiny seeds are one of the richest sources of lignans, linked to powerful protection from breast and prostate cancer.

Flax seeds are simply fabulous for lowering both systolic and diastolic blood pressure. A feature of flax is a group of nutrients called lignans, which have powerful antioxidant and anti-oestrogenic properties and help in preventing breast and prostate cancer, as well as other types of cancer. Please use ground flax as the whole seed is difficult to absorb.

Sesame, pumpkin and sunflower seeds – Sesame seeds are a goldmine of health benefits and are loaded with minerals. Pumpkin seeds are one of the richest sources of zinc among plant foods. Zinc is essential for the proper functioning

(continued)

of many differ types of immune cells. These seeds are also high in vitamin K. Sunflowers are one of the few heliotropic plants (they turn their face to the sun), and heliotropism is thought to aid in growth and photosynthesis. These seeds are very high in protein and vitamin E.

Walnuts are an excellent source of polyphenols and are linked to better brain function and improved memory. Eating walnuts may counter age-related decline and reduce one's risk of neurodegenerative diseases, such as Alzheimer's. They are also a very good source of ALA. Walnuts reduce LDL cholesterol oxidation and have anti-inflammatory effects.

Dried cherries – Tart cherries help with soreness following a workout. Cherries also offer cardiovascular benefits such as lowering C-reactive protein and blood pressure levels.

 Who says a vegan diet is healthy? One myth that dies hard is that nutritional science supports the modern diet built around animal-sourced food. This was certainly true in the past but very wrong in the present. An increasing number of prestigious universities and professional organisations support the shift to a vegan approach to eating.

Consider this list of organisations that state that a **vegan diet** is not only a healthy nutritional approach but that it is **superior to the modern diet**: Harvard School of Public Health; the Cleveland Clinic; New York Presbyterian Hospital; the *Permanente Journal*; Dietitians Association of Australia; Academy of Nutrition and Dietetics; British Dietetic Association; Dietitians of Canada, the Ronald Reagan UCLA Medical Centre; the Mayo Clinic; Nutrition Facts; Walter Willet, the chair of Harvard's Nutrition Department. I think that the argument is over.

One of the features of healthy societies is that they relax at meals and don't overeat. In fact, in Okinawa it is considered very bad manners to eat too much; eating modest amounts of food is considered a sign of a cultured person. In modern culture, food is often eaten on the run. We get used to eating quickly to fit lunch or breakfast into a busy schedule, and as a result don't chew properly. What a mistake. When we stop moving, sit and relax we digest food more efficiently and convert blood sugars for long-term storage. These functions of the parasympathetic nervous system do not function when the mind is anxious.

We think of the environment as something outside of us, but the environment most important to our individual health exists within us. The gut biome is the key to many important aspects of our health. It is made up of the billions of microorganisms that live in our intestinal tract. These tiny lifeforms are a potent influence not only on digestion but also our immune system, nervous system and even the brain. They may be the key to overall health. When we consider the extent of influence these tiny creatures have it is important to remember that the single factor that determines the composition of this internal environment is the food we eat. The species of microbes and their efficient function can be changed radically with a single meal. Guess which way of eating makes them most happy? You got it! A diverse vegan diet creates a happy biome. I refer to this as *Happy Bugs, Happy Me!*

Many people have been led to believe that only animal products like meat, eggs and dairy supply adequate protein. The usual claim is that only these foods contain 'first class' protein. If this is true, how do animals that don't eat other animals get their protein? Gorillas, elephants and oxen all seem to have plenty of protein without eating meat and eggs. The answer is that all protein comes ultimately from plants, in the form of amino acids. These are the building blocks of protein that our body assembles into the tissue that we require for good health. It is an accepted fact that a diverse vegan diet (like the foods in this book) provides all the protein essential for good health.

Dried Berry Granola

This is a delicious recipe and easily adapted to your own likes and dislikes. Get the kids involved making this granola. Works great as a topping for desserts or as a snack. I give this as a gift to family and friends. It looks wonderful in decorative glass jars. Time to spread some vegan joy!

6 cups jumbo organic oats
1 cup mixed nuts, chopped
1 cup mixed seeds
1 cup flaked almonds
1 cup desiccated coconut
Pinch sea salt
¼ tsp cinnamon
1 cup apple juice
½ cup rice syrup
Dried fruit of your choice

Heat the oven to 180°C (350°F), gas 5. Place the oats, nuts, seeds, flaked almonds, coconut, sea salt and cinnamon in a large bowl and mix together. In a small saucepan, warm the apple juice and rice syrup, add to the bowl and mix well. Transfer the mixture to a large rimmed baking sheet and bake for around 30–40 minutes until golden brown and crisp. Every 10 minutes, stir and turn over the mixture to allow even browning. Allow to cool, transfer to a bowl and stir in the dried fruit of your choice. Serve with rice, oat or almond milk and some fresh berries and fruits of the season. Makes 12 servings.

Your body knows the season of the year. Eating a seasonal diet is common sense. Throughout humanity's long evolution we have been locked into the cycles of the seasons. Our bodies expect us to adapt – it is part of our cellular memory. When the climate shifts to a cooler or warmer state we need to make balance by adjusting our food choices and not simply our wardrobes. When we observe the climate and choose foods that match our local season, we will find that local foods meet our health needs as well as reduce the use of foods that are shipped long distances.

Tofu Scramble

Scrambled tofu is an easy-to-digest dish that resembles scrambled eggs. It is delicious and satisfies the need for phytoestrogens. It can also be served as a bean-protein side dish with lunch or dinner. A super brunch for lazy weekend breakfasts. The sweetcorn, peppers and spring onions are optional. Try different vegetables depending on what's in season.

Tahini sauce

2 tbsp tahini
1 tbsp shoyu or tamari
1 clove garlic
1 tsp Dijon mustard
3 tbsp nutritional yeast
½ cup filtered water

Tofu scramble

2 shallots, thinly sliced
½ tsp turmeric
½ cup roasted sweet red pepper, diced
½ cup button mushrooms, thinly sliced
3 spring onions, thinly sliced on the diagonal
1 cup sweetcorn
1 pack organic tofu
1 tbsp shoyu
½ cup filtered water
½ cup nori threads
¼ cup fresh coriander, minced
Parsley, minced for garnish
1 tbsp toasted black sesame seeds

In a high-speed blender, blend the ingredients for the sauce and set aside. In a heavy-based pan, warm a splash or two of filtered water over a medium heat. Add the shallots and turmeric, cover and allow to sweat for 5 minutes. Add the red pepper, mushrooms, spring onions and sweetcorn and sauté for a further 5–8 minutes.

Crumble or mash the tofu into the pan and add the shoyu, along with the half cup of water. Cover and cook for 5 minutes. Stir in the creamy tahini mixture, nori threads and coriander. Stir well and remove from the heat. Sprinkle over the parsley and black sesame seeds. Serve hot piled high on some toasted sourdough or a crusty wholegrain baguette. Makes 4–5 servings.

Sweet or Savoury Buckwheat Crepes

Using just a few plant-based ingredients and no refined sugar or oil, these crepes are flavourful and filling and can be enjoyed sweet or savoury.

¾ cup buckwheat flour
¾ cup unbleached white flour
2 tsp baking powder
2 small ripe bananas, chopped
1½ cups oat or soy milk
½ cup sparkling water
1 tbsp apple cider vinegar
Filtered water as desired

Mix the dry ingredients together in a large bowl. Place the bananas and wet ingredients into a high-speed blender. Blend to create a smooth mixture. Heat a crepe maker or flat pan or griddle to a high heat. Pour on half a cup of the mixture and spread with a crepe spreader. Cook the crepe for 2 to 3 minutes. Bubbles will form and the edges will brown. Carefully push a spatula under the edge of the crepe all the way around. Flip and cook for another few minutes on the other side. Makes 6 large crepes.

Note – If you prefer a thinner crepe, add a little more water to the mixture. Use other flours such as wholewheat pastry flour, or mix the quantities. When blueberries are in season, I add a half-cup to the mixture.

Sweet filling
Banana
Fresh blueberries
Maple or brown rice syrup

Savoury filling
2 cloves garlic
2 onions
12 chestnut mushrooms
1 red or yellow pepper
1 courgette
Tamari
½ cup coriander or parsley, chopped
Pesto
Mayonnaise

Mince the garlic and cut all the vegetables into small dice. Warm a splash or two of filtered water in a heavy-based pan. Sauté the garlic and onion for 5 minutes. Add the vegetables and a splash or two of tamari. Cover and cook for 10 minutes, stirring occasionally and adding more water if the pan seems dry. Stir in the fresh herbs and transfer the vegetables to a covered dish.

Assembling
When the crepe is warm, spread it with some basil and watercress pesto (page 191) and oil-free mayonnaise (page 194). Add your roasted vegetables and roll or fold in half. Enjoy with a warming bowl of soup.

Note – You can, of course, choose to purchase oil-free pesto and mayonnaise.

International trade agreements mean that fuel for international freight carried by sea and air is not taxed, which only encourages supermarkets to import foods from all around the world. For example, the wheat used for bread in the UK often comes from America and has travelled over 4,000 miles; a kiwi fruit in America can have logged up 5,000 miles coming from Chile. Corn from Senegal is in abundance in UK supermarkets all year round. The laying on of '**food miles**' to take advantage of cheap labour undermines the development of local sustainable agriculture. By taking back the food system and cooking our own food at home and using local organic sources we can not only change our health but also contribute to a healthy use of resources and social justice.

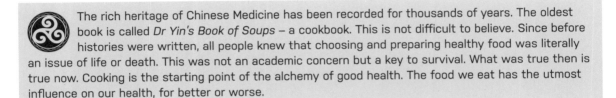 The rich heritage of Chinese Medicine has been recorded for thousands of years. The oldest book is called *Dr Yin's Book of Soups* – a cookbook. This is not difficult to believe. Since before histories were written, all people knew that choosing and preparing healthy food was literally an issue of life or death. This was not an academic concern but a key to survival. What was true then is true now. Cooking is the starting point of the alchemy of good health. The food we eat has the utmost influence on our health, for better or worse.

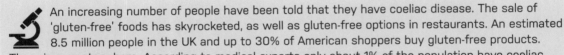 An increasing number of people have been told that they have coeliac disease. The sale of 'gluten-free' foods has skyrocketed, as well as gluten-free options in restaurants. An estimated 8.5 million people in the UK and up to 30% of American shoppers buy gluten-free products. There is a mystery here. According to medical experts only about 1% of the population have coeliac disease, and 6% have gluten sensitivity.

The definitive diagnosis of coeliac disease is made by a bowel biopsy, which can show if there is damage to the lining of the intestine. This process can be supported by blood tests. Without these tests, or tests for wheat allergies, diagnosis is simply a guess. Some are diagnosed with 'wheat sensitivity' – a diagnosis that is very difficult to verify. However, if gluten products are eliminated a person may experience improved general health. In some cases, these improvements are simply down to cutting out unhealthy breads, biscuits and refined-flour products (many containing sugar).

Unless a standard test has confirmed coeliac disease, a person can begin by eliminating all gluten foods, and eventually add in low-gluten foods to the diet once the symptoms are under control, and monitor any level of discomfort. In any case, the incidence of this disease is overstated and is promoted by those interested in high-protein diets.

Sumptuous Soups

Food historians tell us the history of soup is probably as old as the history of cooking. The act of combining various ingredients in a pot to create a nutritious, filling, simple-to-make meal was inevitable. Healthy and healing soups are part of the cooking tradition in every country.

Try to prepare your soup from fresh, organic, in-season and ideally local ingredients. Whether your ingredients are coming freshly grown from your own garden or you've bought them directly from the farmers' market, making the connection between the food you eat and your local environment is important. The food we eat is part of our cultural identity. Eating local foods helps produce a more resilient and sustainable future, both for yourself and for future generations.

- Quick Miso Broth
- Summer Sweetcorn Chowder
- Roasted Squash and Sweet Potato Bisque with Ume Plum and Almond Cream
- Black Bean Soup with Sour Cream and Chives
- Adzuki Bean Soup with Tamari and Ginger
- Tarragon-Scented Parsnip Soup with Sourdough Croutons
- White Bean Soup with Almond Pistou
- Spicy Brown Lentil Soup with Sour Cream
- Chickpea and Vegetable Soup with Crunchy Peanut Butter and Walnut Croutons
- Creamy Mushroom Soup with Savoury Cashew Cream

Note – umami paste organic vegetable stock – I use this tasty and very quick and easy format. Made from the highest quality natural ingredients without the use of yeast extracts, this is a unique creation which can be used in so many of my recipes, from soups to sauces, risottos and stroganoffs.

Quick Miso Broth

Miso is a fermented soybean paste used to flavour various dishes, but most widely used as a stock to season soups. Miso's natural fermentation process creates a combination of enzymes that strengthen and nourish the intestinal tract. As a result, the blood that nourishes the balance of the body is much stronger. The quality of our blood creates the people we are, and the health we possess.

    1 × 4 inch (10 cm) small strip kombu seaweed
    ¼ cup tightly packed dried maitake mushrooms, or 2 dried shiitake mushrooms
    4 cups filtered water
    3 spring onions, thinly sliced
    1 tsp wakame flakes, or a 5 inch (12 cm) piece of pre-soaked wakame cut into small pieces
    4 or 5 heaped tsp miso paste (approx. 1 tsp miso per bowl of soup)
    Juice squeezed from 1 tbsp freshly grated ginger
    Diced spring onion or chives and alfalfa sprouts, for garnish

In a small bowl, cover the wakame flakes, if using, in filtered water and set aside. In a soup pot, soak the kombu and shiitake or maitake mushrooms in two cups of filtered water for 20 minutes. Remove the mushrooms and cut into small pieces. If using shiitake mushrooms, cut off the stems, discard, and thinly slice the caps.

Add another 4 cups of filtered water to the pot. Cover and bring to a boil.

Reduce the heat to a low simmer and cook for 10 minutes. Add the spring onions and wakame flakes or pieces of pre-soaked wakame and cook for 5 minutes. Place the miso paste into a small mesh strainer and lower into the broth; using a spoon, stir until the paste is dissolved. Scrape the residue (grain) into the soup pot. Add the ginger juice to aid in digestion and facilitate the cells' uptake of sugars. Sprinkle the garnish over the soup when serving. Makes 4–6 servings.

Note – This basic miso soup should be a daily staple of your diet. It encompasses the use of sea vegetables to mineralise the blood and a variety of fresh vegetables. The balance of these ingredients creates a strengthening energy vital to life. Miso has been used for centuries in the Orient as a remedy for cancer, weak digestion, low libido and several types of intestinal infections, and to lower cholesterol and so much more, and is one of the world's most medicinal foods. Do not boil the miso – it has so many living microorganisms. You can make a larger batch and store in a glass container in the refrigerator. Take the required amount each morning and gently warm.

Summer Sweetcorn Chowder

A simple sweetcorn chowder recipe for you to cook a great meal for family or friends. Fresh sweetcorn is paired with coconut cream for the ultimate summer comfort food! Using frozen sweetcorn in this quick and easy recipe reduces the cooking time to 20 minutes.

    4 cups organic frozen sweetcorn
    2 heaped tbsp sweet white miso
    4 cups hot filtered water
    1 large onion, chopped
    3 garlic cloves, crushed
    1 cup sweet roasted red bell pepper, cut into small dice
    1 small bunch spring onions, thinly sliced on the diagonal
    2 tsp tamari
    1 cup unsweetened coconut cream
    ¼ cup fresh chives, chopped
    ¼ cup fresh coriander, chopped

In a measuring jug, mix the sweet white miso with the hot water to make a miso stock. Heat a splash or two of filtered water in a large soup pot and sauté the onion and garlic over a low-medium heat for 5 minutes. Add the sweetcorn, red pepper, spring onions, tamari and miso stock. Bring to a boil covered, reduce heat to low and simmer for 15 minutes. Stir in the coconut cream. Place half of the soup mixture into a high-speed blender and blend until smooth. Return to the pot and stir in the fresh chives and coriander. Makes 6 servings.

Roasted Squash and Sweet Potato Bisque with Ume Plum and Almond Cream

This soup is perfect for a cold autumn evening, as a side dish to a meal or as the main course. The ume paste and almond cream add an extra depth of flavour.

4 cups filtered water
1 umami instant stock sachet or organic stock cube
1 large sweet potato
1 butternut squash
Sea salt
5 cloves garlic
1 large onion, finely diced
Toasted flaked almonds
Crisp nori threads
1 tbsp chopped chives

Preheat the oven to 180°C (350°F), gas 4. Mix the stock with 4 cups of boiling filtered water and set aside. Cut the sweet potato and squash in half lengthways. Massage the cut sides with a little sea salt. Place them cut side down in a shallow roasting tin lined with a parchment sheet. Add the garlic cloves (in their paper). Place in the centre of the oven for 35–40 minutes or until the vegetables are tender.

When the vegetables are cool, scoop out the flesh from the potato and squash, discarding the seeds. Peel the garlic and add the cloves to a saucepan with the stock, along with the roasted vegetables and the diced onion. Bring to a boil covered, reduce heat and simmer for 25 minutes, stirring occasionally. Using a high-speed blender, puree until smooth and creamy. Makes 4–6 servings.

Ume plum cream

1½ tbsp ume plum paste
1 cup pomegranate seeds
2 tbsp brown rice syrup
2 tbsp filtered water

Add the ingredients to a high-speed blender and blend to a cream.

Sweet almond cream

½ cup blanched almonds, soaked overnight
½ cup filtered water
1 tbsp brown rice syrup

Drain and rinse the almonds. Add the ingredients to a high-speed blender and blend to a cream.

Serve the soup in warmed bowls. Place some toasted flaked almonds and crisp nori strips in the centre. Make a spiral design with some almond cream, and then an outer circle with some ume cream. Sprinkle over a few cut chives.

Note – I use squeezy bottles, but you can work the same magic simply with the back of a spoon to create the swirls.

Black Bean Soup with Sour Cream and Chives

Beans are the unsung hero. To have the world to fall in love with beans is one of my missions. Black beans don't have a strong flavour of their own, but they do carry other flavours superbly, while at the same time offering a unique velvety texture. Serving sour cream with the soup makes a clever contrast that is appealing to the eye. It's good to remind ourselves that we do in fact eat with our eyes!

3 cups cooked black beans (instructions in the enchiladas recipe on page 132)
1 cup roasted red peppers, cut into small dice
4 shallots, thinly sliced
1 leek, thinly sliced
4 cloves crushed garlic
1 tsp ground cumin
1 tsp dried basil
1 tbsp tamari
1 umami instant stock sachet
3 cups hot filtered water
1 cup fresh or frozen sweetcorn
½ cup fresh coriander, minced
Sour cream (pages 185–186)
Chopped chives for garnish

Dissolve the umami paste in the hot water and set aside. Warm a little filtered water in a heavy-based pan and sauté the peppers, shallots, leek and garlic over medium heat for 10 minutes. Add the cumin, basil and tamari and cook for a further 5 minutes. Add the beans and stock. Bring to a boil uncovered. Reduce the heat and cover; simmer for 20 minutes, adding more water if necessary. Add the sweetcorn and coriander and simmer for a further 5 minutes. Taste and adjust the seasonings. Serve in warmed bowls and add one or two dollops of sour cream. Garnish with fresh chives. Makes 6 servings.

Note – If pressure-cooking or slow-cooking the beans, use the liquid the beans have been cooked in and cut back to one cup of water for the stock. Use a jar of organic beans for quickness – drain and rinse well.

Adzuki Bean Soup with Tamari and Ginger

The ingredients in this soup are easy to keep on hand. The rich, sweet taste belies the ease of preparation. I make this soup at our workshops to balance blood sugar levels and nourish my clients' kidneys. The perfect tonic to relax the pancreas and spleen.

    2 sachets umami instant sock dissolved in 6 cups of hot filtered water
    3 cups cooked adzuki beans
    1 cup each of diced onion, carrot, celery, butternut squash, burdock and parsnip
    4 strips kale (leaves only), thinly sliced
    Juice squeezed from 1 tbsp freshly grated ginger
    Tamari to taste

Garnish
    Lentil and broccoli sprouts
    Finely sliced spring onions

To cook the beans
    1 cup dried adzuki beans
    3 inch (7 cm) piece kombu seaweed

Soak the beans and kombu overnight. Discard the water from the soaked beans. Place the beans and kombu in a pressure cooker with enough fresh filtered water to cover the beans. Bring to full pressure, reduce the heat to low and cook for 30 minutes. Allow the pressure to come down naturally. Place the cooked beans, vegetables (except the kale) and stock in a heavy-based pan and cook over a low heat for 25–30 minutes. Stir in the kale and cook for another 5 minutes. Add the ginger juice and tamari to taste. Garnish with sprouts and spring onions. Makes 4–6 servings.

Note – Presoaking beans significantly reduces cooking time and improves their texture and digestibility.

Note – Adzuki beans are small and very compact, with a deep reddish-brown colour. These tiny beans are a staple in the Far East. They are revered in Japan for their healing properties. They are low in fat and reputed to be more digestible than most other beans, as well as being rich sources of potassium, iron and B vitamins (not B12) and high in protein and fibre. I use these incredibly power-packed nutritional beans to make soups, burgers, medicinal teas, pâtés and desserts. The possibilities are endless.

Tarragon-Scented Parsnip Soup with Sourdough Croutons

I do believe that parsnips are winter's most underrated vegetables. They are busting with vitamins and minerals and, with almost no fat, cholesterol or sodium, are perfect for those reducing their weight. Parsnips are bursting with goodness, being high in fibre, folic acid and potassium, which helps raise energy and reduce blood pressure.

For the sourdough croutons

- 8 slices stale sourdough bread torn into 1 inch (2 cm) pieces
- 1 tbsp Italian seasoning
- ½ tsp garlic powder
- ¼ tsp sea salt

Preheat the oven to 170°C (340°F), gas 4. Remove the crusts, cut the bread into bite-sized cubes and place in a large bowl. Add the seasonings and mix well. Spread evenly on two parchment-lined baking sheets. Bake until the cubes just begin to brown and are crisp, about 5–10 minutes. Cool the cubes on the baking sheets for 20 minutes, and then transfer to an airtight container and store at room temperature for up to 2 weeks.

For the soup

- 1 large onion, diced
- 1 large leek, diced
- 6–8 parsnips, peeled and diced
- 2 cups almond or oat milk
- 2 cups organic vegetable stock
- 2 tbsp rice mirin
- 1 tbsp dried tarragon
- 2 tbsp sweet white miso
- Sourdough croutons

Garnish

- Cress
- Wild lavender garlic flowers

Place the onion, leek and parsnips in a soup pot. Add the plant-based milk, stock, mirin and tarragon. Cover and bring to a boil. Reduce heat and simmer until the parsnips are soft (about 25 minutes). Transfer to a blender and blend to a cream. Dissolve the miso in a half cup of the soup and return to the pan. Serve in warmed bowls and top with croutons. Garnish with some cress and the flowers. Makes 4–6 servings.

White Bean Soup with Almond Pistou

A tasty white bean sweet soup seasoned with garlic and thyme that tastes even better the next day. All bean soups have forever been great for us, and this one has the powerful protein and good quality fat of almonds as the base. Make a double batch and have plenty of leftovers for the weekly dinner rush!

4 spring onions, finely diced
3 cloves fresh garlic, finely minced
Sea salt
2 stalks celery, diced
1 carrot, diced
1½ cups cooked cannellini beans
3 cups unsweetened almond or soy milk
2 heaped tsp vegetable bouillon powder
1 cup hot filtered water
½ tsp dried thyme

Pistou

Although many people think that pistou is simply the French equivalent of Ligurian pesto from Italy, it's not as simple as that. The biggest difference is that there are no pine nuts in French pistou. The basic recipe is Genovese basil and garlic. Use this pistou as a spread; on top of baked potatoes, pizza or vegetables; or added to pasta.

½ cup blanched almonds
2 cloves fresh garlic, sliced
1 cup loosely packed basil leaves
2 tsp sweet white miso
1 tsp brown rice syrup
2 tbsp filtered water

To cook the beans

1 cup dried cannellini beans
2 inch (5 cm) piece of kombu

Wash and soak the beans overnight in filtered water with the kombu. Discard the soaking water and rinse the beans well. Place the beans and kombu in a pressure cooker and cover with 2 inches (5 cm) of water. Bring to a boil, cover and lock lid into position. Bring to full pressure then reduce the heat to medium low. Cook for 30 minutes. Remove from the heat and allow the pressure to drop. Scoop out the kombu, stir the beans and remove one and a half cups for the recipe. Refrigerate or freeze the remaining beans.

Dissolve the vegetable bouillon in the hot water, and set aside. Warm a splash or two of filtered water or dashi stock in a heavy-based pan. Place the spring onions and garlic and a pinch of salt in the pan and sauté until the vegetables are translucent. Stir in the celery and carrot and sauté for 5 minutes. Spread the vegetables over the bottom of the pan and top with the beans. Add the almond or soy milk, vegetable bouillon, cup of hot water, and dried thyme. Cover and bring to a boil over a medium heat. Reduce heat to low and cook for 15 minutes. Makes 4–6 servings.

While the soup cooks, make the pistou. Place all the ingredients into a food processor and purée until smooth. Add more water to reach the desired consistency.

To serve, ladle the soup into individual bowls and top with a hearty dollop of pistou.

Spicy Brown Lentil Soup with Sour Cream

Super-healthy vegetables are bathed in a bowl of low-fat lentil soup in this easy winter warmer. This soup is a classic recipe that will work with pretty much any legume. I like to make mine with dried brown lentils. Brown lentils, even red and yellow (albeit the soup colour will look quite different), chickpeas and other beans will all work great with this recipe.

2 tbsp vegetable stock or filtered water
2 shallots, finely chopped
1 leek, very finely sliced
1 small squash, cut into small cubes
1 courgette, cut into small cubes
1 sweet potato, peeled and cut into small cubes
1 parsnip, peeled and cut into small cubes
1 cup fresh or frozen sweetcorn
Pinch sea salt
2 tsp dried basil
1 tsp ground cumin
1 tbsp ground coriander
½ tsp chilli powder (optional)
2 umami instant stock sachets dissolved in 6 cups filtered water
1½ cups brown lentils (rinsed and soaked for 30 minutes)
Shoyu to taste
Sour cream (pages 185–186)
Chopped parsley or coriander

Heat the water or stock in a large pot and cook the shallots and leek over a low heat for 5–7 minutes. Add the squash, courgette, sweet potato, parsnip, sweetcorn, salt, basil and spices and cook for 5 minutes. Pour in the stock, cover and bring to the boil. Add the lentils and cook on a low heat, covered, for 20–25 minutes until the soup starts to thicken. Add more water to reach the desired consistency. Using a stick blender, half-purée the soup so it's thick and creamy but not completely smooth. Adjust the seasoning with shoyu or tamari if desired. Serve in warmed bowls topped with some sour cream. Garnish with chopped parsley or coriander and serve with warmed naan bread. Makes 6–8 servings.

Chickpea and Vegetable Soup with Crunchy Peanut Butter and Walnut Croutons

This chickpea and red lentil soup with herby toasted walnuts and a bit of crunchy peanut butter is just bursting with flavour.

1 red onion, diced
2 celery stalks, cut into small dice
2 carrots, cut into small dice
1 tsp ground cumin
1 tsp ground coriander
1 tsp turmeric
2 cloves garlic, crushed
1 cup red lentils, rinsed
1½ cups cooked chickpeas (see classic hummus recipe, pages 186–187)
1 umami instant stock sachet dissolved in 4 cups warm filtered water
3 tbsp crunchy peanut butter
2 courgettes, cut into small dice
1 tbsp tamari
Walnut croutons

In a heavy-based pan, sauté the onion, celery and carrots in a little filtered water or stock. Cook over a medium heat for 5 minutes. Add the spices and garlic and a splash of water and cook for a further few minutes. Add the lentils and cooked chickpeas, along with the stock. Mix well, then stir in the peanut butter and courgettes. Bring to a boil, turn down to a low simmer and cover. Cook for 25 minutes. Stir in the tamari and adjust seasonings to taste. Serve topped with some walnut croutons. Makes 6 servings.

Walnut croutons
½ cup walnuts
1 tsp tamari
1 tbsp nutritional yeast
¼ tsp onion powder
¼ tsp garlic powder
Pinch or two sea salt

Preheat oven to 140°C (275°F), gas 1. Place the walnuts in a mixing bowl. Drizzle with tamari and stir to coat. In a separate bowl, mix together all the other ingredients. Sprinkle over the nuts and stir to combine. Spread on a parchment-lined baking sheet and roast for 5–8 minutes or until crisp, taking care that the nuts don't burn.

Creamy Mushroom Soup with Savoury Cashew Cream

The secret to this rich soup is to use a combination of dried and fresh mushrooms. This will give the soup a much richer colour and flavour. You only require a small portion to feel satisfied by the deep earthy flavours.

For the savoury cashew cream
½ cup cashews, soaked overnight
¼ cup filtered water
1 tsp fresh lemon juice
1 tsp ume plum seasoning

Place cashews in a bowl, cover with filtered water and soak overnight. Rinse and place the drained cashews in a high-speed blender. Add the remaining ingredients. Blend on high until super smooth. You might have to stop to scrape down the blender now and then, or add a touch more water. Thin to your desired consistency. Transfer into a small airtight container and chill in the fridge to thicken.

For the soup
3 dried shiitake mushrooms
½ cup dried maitake mushrooms
2 cups fresh mushrooms, such as shiitake and white button, chopped
1 cup spring onions, finely chopped
Ground black pepper (optional) to taste
½ tsp dried dill
2 cloves garlic, minced
1 tbsp freshly squeezed lemon juice
2 tbsp rice mirin
1 umami instant stock sachet dissolved in 2 cups warm filtered water
1 tbsp plain flour
½ cup savoury cashew cream, plus a little more for garnish
2 tbsp chives, minced

Soak the dried mushrooms in 4 cups of lukewarm filtered water for one hour. Drain and reserve the soaking water to use as part of the stock. This will give the soup a delicious umami taste. Slice all the mushrooms, discarding the stems from the dried shiitakes. Warm a splash or two of water in a heavy-based pot. Add the mushrooms, spring onions, pepper, dill, garlic and lemon juice. Cook for 2 minutes, stirring frequently. Increase the heat slightly and add the rice mirin. Simmer for 3 minutes, or until the liquid is reduced slightly. Whisk the flour into the mixture along with a splash or two of water, stirring well to avoid lumping.

(continued)

Add the stock and soaking liquid from the dried mushrooms. Bring to a boil and reduce the heat to medium low. Cover and simmer for 30 minutes. Transfer to a blender and purée until smooth. Return to the pot and add the cashew cream. Add extra water to achieve your desired consistency. Serve in warm bowls and add two or three swirls of the cream and the minced chives. Makes 4–6 servings.

Note – If you don't have maitake mushrooms, add one extra dried shiitake mushroom. Dried shiitake and maitake mushrooms are one of my 'top-drawer' foods of excellence. They are incredible immune boosters. They add mouth-watering umami flavour to your dishes. They have an intensely earthy taste, so a few go a long way. I use these incredible mushrooms for lowering my clients' cholesterol and triglyceride levels and for cleansing the blood.

An incredible 85% of agricultural land on earth is given over to **feeding and housing animals** for food. This is a tragic situation. We are using about 60% more land than we need to feed the world. In order to feed the constantly growing number of animals, to satisfy our appetite for meat, we are cutting down more forests. This levelling of forests is done mostly in South America and Asia, far from the eyes of America and Europe. These forests are a protection between us and a toxic atmosphere. Eating a diet rich in animal-sourced foods contributes to the poisoning of the air we breathe.

Quick Bites

Whether lunch or dinner is looming, you can take your pick from these quick bites. Add a fresh salad from my lip-smacking sides and salads section, or choose one of my sumptuous filling soups.

- Grilled Portobello and Roasted Red Pepper Sandwich
- Mediterranean Chickpea Salad Sandwich
- Vegan Bean Burritos
- Vegan California (Uramaki-Style) Sushi Roll with Ginger-Tamari Dipping Sauce
- Crispy Sweet and Sour Tempeh Sourdough Sandwich

Grilled Portobello and Roasted Red Pepper Sandwich

The best portobello sandwich our students say they ever had! Done correctly, a grilled portobello sandwich can be one of the heartiest, most delicious sandwiches. Here's how to do it.

2 tbsp balsamic vinegar
2 tbsp shoyu
3 garlic cloves, minced
1 tbsp freshly squeezed ginger juice
2 tbsp filtered water
4 portobello mushrooms, cleaned and stems removed
½ cup roasted red pepper, chopped
½ cup oil-free mayonnaise (page 194)
2 tbsp chopped chives
4 sourdough baguettes, toasted

Filling
4 tomatoes, thinly sliced
Fresh salad greens, rocket, arugula, etc.
½ cup roasted red pepper, thinly sliced

Mix the first five ingredients together in a bowl. Place the mushroom caps in a container. Pour over the marinade, seal with a lid and set aside for at least two hours to marinate. Shake the container to make sure the mushrooms are well coated. In a small bowl, mix the red pepper with the mayonnaise and chopped chives, and set aside. Preheat the grill to medium. Place the mushrooms, gill side down, on a parchment-lined baking sheet. Grill for 4–5 minutes on each side. Place the baguettes, cut side down, on the grill rack and toast each side. Spread the mayonnaise mixture on the base of each baguette. Top with the mushroom, tomato, salad greens and some roasted red pepper slices. Dress with some relish of your choice if desired. Makes 4 sandwiches.

Mediterranean Chickpea Salad Sandwich

This Mediterranean-style chickpea salad sandwich is colourful and bursting with flavour. You can also top with some pickled red onions and mashed avocado. Use this chickpea mixture in lettuce wraps, on a bed of leafy greens with sliced cucumbers and tomatoes, or scoop up with crackers or vegetable crudités.

Sprouted bread
1 cup hummus (pages 186–187)
3 cups cooked chickpeas
1 small red onion, shaved
½ cup grilled artichoke hearts, thinly sliced
½ cup Kalamata olives, halved
½ cup celery, thinly sliced
1 tsp dried dill
1 tsp garlic granules
1 tbsp ume seasoning
¼ cup chopped chives
Watercress

To cook the chickpeas

2 cups dried chickpeas

Rinse the chickpeas, place in a large bowl and cover with filtered water to soak overnight. Drain and transfer the chickpeas to the pressure cooker. Use enough water to cover the beans – about 1 inch (2 cm). Bring to full pressure, then reduce heat to medium low. Cook for 50 minutes. Turn off the heat and allow the pressure to release naturally. Remove the chickpeas from the pressure cooker and leave to cool.

In a large mixing bowl, add the cooked chickpeas to the hummus. Using the back of a fork, or potato masher, roughly mash about ¾ of the chickpeas, leaving some whole. Add in the remaining ingredients and mix well to combine. Make your sandwich on soft or toasted sprouted bread. Store leftovers in the refrigerator for up to a week in an airtight container. Makes 6–8 sandwiches.

Note – Sprouted bread is a type of bread made from whole grains that have been allowed to sprout – that is, to germinate – before being milled into flour. There are a few different types of sprouted-grain bread. Some are made with additional added flour; some are made with added gluten; and some, such as Essene bread, are made with very few additional ingredients.

Vegan Bean Burritos

A Mexican fiesta of a recipe, these vegetable-filled burritos are packed full of flavour and texture. This hearty dish is easy to make and is the perfect option to fill you up. These burritos are *soooo* good, you'll want to have them every night. Corn tortillas are wrapped around the hearty bean mixture, sour cream, salsa, avocado slices and coriander.

6 organic corn tortillas
2 cups cooked black bean mixture
1 medium avocado, sliced
Salsa (pages 187–188)
Sour cream (pages 185–186)
2 limes, cut into wedges
Fresh coriander, chopped

To cook the black bean mixture

1 cup onions, chopped
Pinch sea salt
1 tbsp minced garlic
½ cup roasted red pepper, chopped
2 cups cooked black beans (instructions in enchiladas recipe on pages 132–134)
½ cup bean liquid

Warm a splash or two of filtered water in a heavy-based pan over a medium heat. Add the onions, sea salt, minced garlic and roasted red pepper. Cook the mixture for 5 minutes, then add the cooked beans along with the bean liquid. Cook for 15 minutes until the onions and pepper are soft. Transfer to a large bowl. Use the back of a fork to partially mash the beans, leaving about half whole.

Warm the tortillas in a dry pan, stacking them on a plate covered with a damp paper towel as you go. Fill the tortillas with the black bean mixture and top with avocado slices, salsa and sour cream. Serve with lime wedges and fresh coriander. Makes 6 burritos.

Note – Refrigerate or freeze any leftover beans from the pressure cooker.

Vegan California (Uramaki-Style) Sushi Roll with Ginger-Tamari Dipping Sauce

We adore making all sorts of nori rolls with rice and vegetable fillings – easy and quick to assemble. California rolls are made with the sushi rice on the outside and the nori on the inside.

California rolls

2 cups cooked sushi rice
4 sheets toasted nori
1–2 tsp umeboshi paste
1 small carrot, cut into strips
¼ cucumber, cut into strips
1 avocado, sliced
Roasted red pepper, sliced
1 tbsp toasted sesame seeds (optional)

To cook the sushi rice

3 cups sushi rice
3 cups filtered water

Place the rice in a large bowl. Add water and gently stir the rice with your hand. When it becomes cloudy, pour the water away and repeat until it becomes clear. Soak the rice for 30 minutes, then drain. Add the rice and water to a heavy-based saucepan. Bring to the boil, cover and cook low heat for 15 minutes. Remove and leave the rice to soften for a further 10–15 minutes, then mix well.

Lay down a sushi mat and cover with biodegradable cling film. Place a nori sheet shiny side up. Place one-quarter of the cooled rice into the middle of the nori sheet.

Using a paddle (or wet fingers) gently push the rice outwards to the edges and corners. Leave a tiny space of nori at the top and bottom of the sheet. Pick up the nori sheet from the bottom and, holding tightly, flip it over so that the rice is underneath. Lay a strips of cucumber, carrot, avocado or pepper on the nori sheet. Spread them so they fill the entire roll lengthwise. Spread a little umeboshi paste over the filling.

Hold the bottom of the sushi mat and bring it up and over, creating a tube. Make one roll so that you cannot see your filling. Tuck and squeeze the mat under with your fingers.

Roll your nori sheet up to the end. Squeeze it firmly and evenly all across the mat. When you get to the end, seal the roll evenly. If you want, sprinkle sesame seeds over the top and bottom of the roll and use the sushi mat to press the seeds into the roll. Flip your sushi roll over so the seam side is facing down. Wet a sharp knife and make 6–8 cuts to the sushi roll to create sushi pieces. Makes 24–32 rolls.

Ginger-tamari dipping sauce

2 tbsp tamari or shoyu
2 tbsp filtered water
¼ tsp grated fresh ginger

Mix ingredients together and place in individual serving bowls.

Crispy Sweet and Sour Tempeh Sourdough Sandwich

Tempeh only tastes as good as what's around it. This sandwich blends the flavours and textures in delicious harmony. I love a texture that crosses into two categories, a blend of crunchy and chewy. This sandwich will hit the spot.

    200 g block of tempeh, sliced into thin strips
    3 tbsp balsamic vinegar
    2 tbsp maple syrup
    1 tbsp tamari
    1 garlic clove, crushed
    ½ tsp paprika
    Bread or bun, toasted
    Oil-free mayonnaise (page 194)
    Red onion, slivers
    Lettuce leaves
    Sauerkraut
    Sprouts of choice

Place the tempeh strips in a single layer into a shallow dish. In a small bowl, whisk together the vinegar, maple syrup, tamari, garlic and paprika. Pour the mixture over the tempeh to cover, and let marinate for 1 hour, flipping the tempeh once or twice to coat all the slices. Preheat the grill to 200°C (400°F), gas 6. Remove the tempeh from the marinade and place on the grill. Cook until golden and crispy, about 7–8 minutes per side.

Toast the bread. Spread one half of the bread with a generous portion of mayonnaise and add some sauerkraut and sprouts. Place cooked tempeh slices on top, followed by lettuce leaves, and top with some shaved red onion, some more sauerkraut and sprouts. Makes 4 sandwiches.

One feature of macrobiotic food wisdom is that the morphology, or form, of a plant indicates certain nutritional features. This is part of the study of yin and yang in Chinese medicine. Foods that are dense in structure and have a more compact form and less moisture are generally considered to have a more yang quality. These foods are believed to be thermogenic, or heat producing. In the West, foods classified as warming include cayenne or chilli pepper: these spices create a dramatic, quick and short-lived warming response. In the macrobiotic classifications, many root vegetables, cabbage and beans have heat-producing qualities. The effect is simply slower and longer lasting. A stew with adzuki beans, carrots, parsnip and onion, with a little ginger, on a cold day will keep you warm for hours.

Some of my heroes – like Dennis Burkitt, Nathan Pritikin, John Yudkin – and many other early pioneers of a more natural way of eating were ridiculed for this during their life. Even 40 years ago, the idea that diet was a major factor in causing disease was considered to be absurd – the primary causes were felt to be viral or bacterial. These beliefs were based on very prejudiced and often faulty science. Even when the truth of nutritional impact was obvious. and expressed by such giants as Dr John McDougall, there was a bias to look for another cause. Part of this was a desire to please the food industry.

The work of these pioneers could have saved the lives of countless people, but instead was hidden away in the service of greed. Unfortunately, commercial interests still have massive power to influence the quality of food. The lower on the food chain you eat, the better you empower local and smaller farmers, as well as having more control over your food.

Many people see fish farms as an answer to feeding the world. They are not. Anyone seeing the water quality in a fish farm would be repulsed. Packing in the maximum number of fish (to maximise profits) means these farms are a breeding ground for disease. Similar to other intensive animal farming, the threat of disease means that massive amounts of antibiotics are given to the fish. Last but not least, one of the most popular farmed fish is salmon. Salmon is a carnivore, it eats other fish and shellfish. In order to feed the farmed salmon, small fish are netted by the ton to make fish meal to feed them. This destroys the ocean food chain.

Big Bowls

If you haven't already hopped aboard the bowl train, I have included seven of my favourite recipes that we thrive on. My hearty bowls are packed with vegetables and warming flavours, perfect for all seasons. I have created some family favourites using the short-grain brown rice I love as the base for the various toppings. For the chilli bowl, vegetable seitan bowl and lemon-infused baked tofu bowl, please use the recipe below to cook the short-grain brown rice. Yummy, comforting bowls at every sitting are guaranteed.

- Three Bean Chilli Bowl
- Rice and Corn Fusilli Bowl with Broccoli and Lemon Cashew Sauce
- Yakisoba Bowl
- Millet Sesame-Crusted Tempeh Veggie Bowl with Sweet Peanut Sauce
- Vegetable Seitan Rice Bowl
- Lemon-Infused Baked Tofu Brown Rice Bowl
- Ramen Bowl with Fresh Daikon and Greens

For the bowls in this section that include rice

Rinse two cups of rice and soak overnight. Discard the soaking water. Place the rice in a heavy-based pot. Add 4 cups of water and bring to a boil. Add a pinch of sea salt. Cover, place a flame spreader under the pot, reduce heat to low, and simmer for 30–40 minutes, or until all water is absorbed. Yields enough freshly cooked rice to make 4–6 bowls.

Three Bean Chilli Bowl

This flavourful three bean chilli is easy to adjust to your preferred spice level and delicious topped with sour cream and fresh coriander. This is also delicious as a filling for baked or steamed potatoes or wraps, or served with other grains and vegetables.

4 cups cooked short-grain brown rice (see above)

For the chilli

1 large carrot, chopped into small dice
1 large stick celery, chopped into small dice
1 medium onion, finely chopped
3 cloves garlic, finely chopped
1 tbsp tomato purée
1 tsp ground cumin
1 tsp ground coriander
1 bay leaf
1 cinnamon stick
1 tsp regular or smoked paprika
½ tsp dried chilli flakes (optional)
2 cups tomatoes, diced
1 sweet orange pepper, cut into small dice
1 tbsp tamari
1 cup each cooked kidney beans, pinto beans and black beans
1 cup umami instant stock
Sour cream (pages 185–186)
Handful of chopped coriander leaves
Slices of lime for serving

To cook the beans

½ cup each dried kidney, pinto and black beans
Small piece kombu

Place the beans and kombu in a large bowl and cover with filtered water. Soak overnight. Drain the water and transfer to a pressure cooker. Add fresh water to cover the beans, about 2 inches (5 cm) above the beans. Bring to full pressure then reduce the heat and cook for 40 minutes. Allow the pressure to come down naturally.

Warm a splash or two of filtered water in a heavy-based pan. Add the carrot, celery, onion and garlic. Cook on a medium-hot heat and sweat until the onions are translucent, about 10 minutes. Add the tomato purée and stir to coat the vegetables, then add the cumin, coriander, bay leaf, cinnamon, paprika and dried chilli flakes (if using).

Stir-fry for a minute or two, then add the chopped tomatoes, chopped pepper and tamari. Bring to a simmer, cover and leave on a low heat for 10–20 minutes, stirring occasionally, until the vegetables are cooked through. Stir in the cooked beans, along with the umami stock. Bring back to a simmer, cover and cook on a low heat for 10–15 minutes until the beans are hot. Add chopped coriander leaves and serve with a portion of cooked short-grain brown rice, lime slices and a dollop of sour cream. Makes 4–6 servings.

Rice and Corn Fusilli with Broccoli and Lemon Cashew Sauce

Rice and corn fusilli is a tasty and nutritious alternative to wheat pasta, made from just corn and rice flour. Delicious served with your favourite pasta sauce. Purchase an organic fusilli free from artificial colours, flavours or preservatives, naturally wheat free and gluten free for those who are sensitive to wheat.

2 small heads of broccoli, cut into bite-sized pieces
3 cups fusilli pasta
1 cup cashews, soaked overnight
1½ cups filtered water
3 cloves garlic, minced
3 shallots, thinly sliced
2 tbsp sweet white miso
1 tbsp tamari or shoyu
1 tbsp lemon juice
3 tbsp nutritional yeast
2 tsp light tahini
Black sesame seeds for garnish

Steam the broccoli in a steamer basket over boiling water for about 5 minutes. It should be bright green and still slightly crisp. Cook the pasta in boiling water until just tender, drain and cover with wet paper towels to keep it from becoming sticky. Pop the lid back on the pot and set aside. Drain the soaking water from the cashews and process along with the filtered water in the blender until smooth. In a heavy-based pan, sauté the garlic and shallots in a little water for 5 minutes. Add the cashew mixture, miso, tamari, lemon juice, nutritional yeast and tahini. Cook over a low heat for 10 minutes, stirring occasionally. Blend to a cream in a high-speed blender. Divide the pasta between four bowls and top with the broccoli. Pour over some of the sauce and garnish with black sesame seeds. Makes 4–6 servings.

Yakisoba Bowl

Yakisoba brings an eclectic mix of oriental dining to the heart of your table. Yakisoba, literally 'fried buckwheat', is a Japanese noodle stir-fry dish. Although soba means buckwheat, yakisoba noodles are actually made from wheat flour. Whether in the form of udon, soba, yakisoba, somen, the universally popular ramen or other forms, Japan's love affair with noodles is rich and varied.

For the sauce

    2 tbsp shoyu
    1 tbsp lemon juice
    1 tbsp filtered water
    2 tsp ginger juice
    1 tbsp mirin

Make sauce by combining the ingredients in a small bowl, and set aside.

Yakisoba

    1 pack soba noodles
    1 cup sliced onion (thin half-moons)
    Few pinches sea salt
    ½ cup fresh shiitake mushrooms, thinly
        sliced
    ½ cup carrots, sliced into thin
        matchsticks
    1 cup sugar snap peas
    1 cup celery, thinly sliced on the diagonal
    1 cup mung bean sprouts
    Fresh coriander

In a large pot, cook the soba noodles according to the directions on the package. Drain and wash well with cold water. Set aside. In a large wok, heat a splash or two of water and sauté the onions with a few pinches of sea salt for 4–5 minutes, until translucent.

Add the mushrooms, carrots and celery and keep sautéing for 3–4 more minutes. Add the sugar snap peas and continue sautéing, mixing all the vegetables well in the wok. Add the soba noodles on top of the vegetables, cover and steam for a few minutes on a medium-low flame. If the bottom of the wok is dry, add a little water before covering. Open the cover, pour in the sauce, and toss the bean sprouts over the vegetables. Still over a low flame, mix the noodles and vegetables together using tongs. Mix gently so that the noodles don't break, but the sauce penetrates all the ingredients. Adjust the flavour if necessary by adding a splash or two of shoyu. Garnish with fresh coriander. Makes 4–6 servings.

Variations – You may also use udon or other types of noodles. If you are gluten-sensitive, use brown rice or quinoa noodles.

Millet Sesame-Crusted Tempeh Veggie Bowl with Sweet Peanut Sauce

Although millet is most often thought of as the main ingredient in bird seed, it is not just 'for the birds'. Creamy like mashed potatoes or fluffy like rice, millet is a delicious grain that can accompany many types of food.

For the millet

1 cup millet
2 cups filtered water

Toast the millet in a large, dry saucepan over a medium heat for 4–5 minutes or until it turns a rich golden brown and the grain becomes fragrant. Add the water to the pan and stir well.

Increase the heat to high and bring the mixture to a boil. Lower the heat and simmer covered for 15 minutes. Remove from the heat and keep covered for another 15 minutes. Fluff with a fork and serve warm.

For the peanut sauce

½ cup organic smooth unsalted peanut butter
1 tsp shoyu or tamari
1 tsp brown rice vinegar
½ tsp freshly squeezed ginger juice
1 clove garlic
¼ cup brown rice syrup
¼ to ½ cup warm filtered water

Place all the ingredients into a high-speed blender and blend to a cream, adding more water if you desire a thinner consistency. Transfer to a pouring jug and set aside to allow the flavours to develop.

For the sesame-crusted tempeh

200 g pack tempeh
2 tbsp tamari
2 tsp hot sauce like sriracha (optional, if you like a hot taste)
2 garlic cloves, minced
1 tbsp freshly squeezed ginger juice
Juice from one lemon
2 tbsp brown rice syrup
¼ cup white sesame seeds

For the garnish

Red radishes, thinly sliced

Preheat the oven to 190°C (375°F), gas 5. Cut the tempeh into ½ inch (1 cm) slices and place in a flat glass dish. In a small bowl, combine the tamari, hot sauce (if using), garlic, ginger, lemon juice and brown rice syrup. Whisk to combine and pour over the tempeh. Cover the glass dish and refrigerate for 30 minutes. Put the sesame seeds into a shallow bowl. Remove the tempeh from the marinade. Dip each side of each piece of tempeh in the sesame seeds and set on a baking sheet lined with some parchment paper. Bake for 10 minutes, turn over and bake ten minutes on the other side, until crisp and golden.

Serve on a bed of millet and steamed greens, topped with some lemon-scented arame sauté (page 173). Pour over a generous serving of the peanut sauce. Garnish with red radishes. Makes 4–6 servings.

Note – This also makes great 'bento' lunches, delicious to eat cold the following day. Use also in sandwiches stacked with fresh salad greens, cucumber and vegan mayo.

Vegetable Seitan Rice Bowl

Seitan is a well-known meat replacer, based on wheat proteins, which resembles meat in its structure. The processing of the wheat flour is a natural process, no chemicals are added.

Seitan is produced by boiling the gluten (wheat proteins) in a bouillon, rich in minerals, based on soy sauce and ginger. This combination results in a high mineral content in the seitan in a very high digestibility of the proteins. Seitan is high in fibre, low in calories, easily digestible, and contains no cholesterol or saturated fatty acids. Serve over rice, soba or udon noodles. If seitan is not readily available, substitute with marinated tofu pieces or tempeh.

For the rice bowl
4 cups cooked short-grain brown rice (see instructions in introduction to this chapter)

For the seitan
Step one
200 g pack seitan
½ cup apple juice
1 tbsp shoyu
½ cup filtered water
2 tbsp kuzu (dissolved in 4 tbsp filtered water)
1 tsp fresh ginger juice
Dash of umeboshi seasoning
2 tsp brown rice syrup

Step two
2 cloves fresh garlic, crushed
1 large red onion, finely sliced
1 cup red pepper, thinly sliced
1 cup orange pepper, thinly sliced
1 cup fresh shiitake or button mushrooms, thinly sliced
¼ cup fresh coriander, chopped

For broccoli spears
1 bunch broccoli spears, sliced

To garnish
Spring onions, thinly sliced on the bias

Cut the seitan into thin strips. Warm a heavy-based pan and stir-fry the strips with the ingredients from step one. Cover and cook for 15 minutes over a low heat, adding a little more water if the pan seems dry. Add the garlic, onion, peppers and mushrooms and cook for a further 10 minutes. Stir in the coriander. Bring a small amount of water to a boil. Pop the broccoli spears in the steamer basket and steam for 4–5 minutes until vibrant green. Serve the seitan in bowls atop the rice, and garnish with steamed broccoli spears and spring onions. Makes 4–6 servings.

Lemon-Infused Baked Tofu Brown Rice Bowl

A very versatile recipe that works well in sandwiches, salads and rice bowls, this baked tofu brown rice bowl is high in plant-based protein, fibre, vitamins and minerals and tastes fantastic. With layers of flavour and texture from marinated baked tofu, fresh carrot, crisp mange tout, chewy brown rice, crunchy black sesame seeds and creamy sauce, you'll love how these delicious ingredients and textures come together.

For the rice bowl

4 cups cooked short-grain brown rice (instructions in introduction to this chapter)

For the tofu

250 g pack firm organic tofu
3 garlic cloves, minced
2 tbsp tamari
2 tbsp mirin
1 tbsp lemon juice
1 tbsp freshly grated ginger juice
2 tbsp balsamic vinegar
1 tbsp brown rice syrup
1 tsp sriracha (optional, if you desire a hot sensation)
½ cup filtered water
1 tbsp sesame seeds

Blanched vegetables

2 carrots
2 cups mange tout

Toppings

Lemon and lime tahini sauce (pages 191–192)
Black sesame seeds
Blanched carrots and mange tout
Fresh coriander

To make the tofu

Make the marinade by combining all the ingredients except the tofu together and set aside. Wrap the block of tofu in a clean towel, place it on a plate and cover with another plate. Place something heavy on top of the plate and leave for 1 hour. This will squeeze the water out. Cut the tofu into slabs about ½ inch (1 cm) thick, then cut into squares. Place in a dish and pour the marinade over the tofu. Shake well to cover all the cubes. Cover and refrigerate overnight.

Preheat the oven 170°C (340°F), gas 4. Line a baking sheet with parchment paper and place the tofu cubes in a single layer. Bake for 8–10 minutes, then turn the tofu over and bake on the other side for 5 minutes, until golden brown.

Blanch the carrots and mange tout in a pot of boiling water for 1 minute. Remove and drain. Rinse under cold water.

To serve, divide the rice among four to six bowls. Top with tofu and drizzle over a generous amount of lemon and lime tahini sauce. Top with the carrots, mange tout and some black sesame seeds. Makes 4–6 servings.

Note – If using in sandwiches, cut the tofu into slices and not cubes.

Ramen Bowl with Fresh Daikon and Greens

Ramen is a Japanese dish. It consists of Chinese-style wheat noodles served in a broth, often flavoured with soy sauce or miso, and uses toppings such as dried seaweed and spring onions. This is a deeply satisfying Japanese dish consisting of a powerful broth full of umami, as well as textural noodles and various add-ins. This daikon noodle ramen bowl is my macrobiotic interpretation, with a nice balance of comforting and refreshing flavours and a full-bodied amazing-tasting umami broth.

250 g pack of organic ramen noodles
5 garlic cloves, crushed
1 inch (2 cm) piece ginger, sliced
1 chilli, seeded and sliced (optional)
5 inch (12 cm) piece kombu seaweed
1 cup spring onions, sliced (reserve some for garnish)
3 dried shiitake mushrooms
1 tsp ground turmeric
4 black garlic cloves, sliced
1 cup fresh shiitake mushrooms, thinly sliced
1 tbsp tamari
½ tbsp mirin
¼ cup dried wakame seaweed flakes
300 g pack soft tofu, cubed

Garnish

Spring onions, sliced
1 small daikon radish, grated
Fresh greens
Red radishes, thinly sliced
White sesame seeds

Cook the noodles according to the instructions on the package. In a medium soup pot, combine 8 cups of filtered water with the crushed garlic cloves, ginger, chilli (if using), kombu, spring onions, dried shiitake and turmeric. Leave to soak for at least 1 hour. (I prefer to soak overnight to develop the deep flavour of this delicious umami broth.) Bring to a boil over a medium-high heat. Reduce the heat and simmer partially covered for 30 minutes. Remove from heat, cover and let infuse further while cooking the mushrooms.

In a large pan, warm a splash of filtered water and sauté the black garlic and mushrooms for 7–8 minutes, until all the liquid released by the mushrooms has evaporated. Add tamari and mirin and cook for another 2 minutes, until all the liquid is absorbed. Remove from the heat and set aside. Strain the broth (liquid from soaking the vegetables), pour it back into the pot and turn the heat to medium. Reserve the rehydrated dried shiitake and discard the rest of the solids strained from the broth.

Slice the rehydrated shiitake and add back into the broth. Add the sautéed mushroom mixture to the pot and cook over a low heat for 3–5 minutes. Stir in the wakame seaweed and tofu cubes and simmer for 5 minutes. Taste-test and add a splash more tamari if desired. Serve garnished with sliced spring onion, grated daikon, fresh greens and red radishes. Sprinkle over some white sesame seeds. Store the leftovers in the refrigerator for up to 3 days. Makes 4–6 servings.

In most agricultural societies, cereal grains were considered a gift from the gods. This probably reflects the fact that grains were the food most essential for survival. By basing a diet on grain, the land is most productive and can feed more people. When we take into account the health, environmental and sustainability issues of principal foods, grains come out the best. They are literally 'life-saving' crops. The fact that grain can be stored easily and used throughout the year is also an important factor. The native cultures of the Americas revered maize, Asian cultures rice and Africans millet. It was 'Give us this day our daily bread' – not our daily cheese.

Vitamin B12 is often mentioned as a problem for those who do not consume animal products. It is a curious problem, since the assumption is that animals make the B12 that we need, but that is not true. B12 is made by bacteria. Animals are supplied the vitamin when eating raw and unprocessed vegetation, or even from drinking from streams. Many animals have the bacteria in the gut that produce B12, and this includes humans. The problem is that humans produce B12 in the wrong location for absorption. Many health products are fortified with B12, such as nutritional yeast, or you may supplement with the product as made by the bacteria. A very small amount is needed for the basic requirement to be met. Methylcobalamin is a natural form of the vitamin made by bacterial culture. It is generally considered the most absorbable form of the vitamin.

Your best source of vitamin D is the sun. Vitamin D is a fat-soluble vitamin. It aids in the absorption of calcium, for strong bones. Deficiency may cause rickets and osteomalacia (softening of the bones). Vitamin D is produced in the skin after exposure to UV (ultraviolet) light. A daily walk or sitting in the sun for an hour or so with some exposed skin will usually be enough. Many people get the vitamin from enriched foods such as almond or rice milk. One of the few food sources for the vitamin is mushrooms. Any species of mushrooms has the capacity to provide vitamin D. Wild mushrooms should contain good levels of the vitamin, but cultivated mushrooms are almost always grown in the dark, so don't contain high levels. However, if you leave them outside in the sun for a few hours (not behind glass, as that blocks the UV), their vitamin D levels will rise dramatically. Shiitake mushrooms, one of my favourites, are especially effective at this trick. Simply place fresh mushrooms in the sun with the gills side up. (You still need to get in the sun no matter how many mushrooms you eat.)

Global-Fusion Main Events

We have had students from 27 countries graduate on our Macrobiotic Health Coach Programme. In the practical session of their assessment, each student has taught a dish from their own culture. This presentation forms part of their certification. They all agree that you can continue to enjoy the comfort food, curries and healthy meals that are synonymous with your own culture, just as they did. Simply make all your favourite dishes the vegan way. I am confident you'll find plenty enticing recipes to inspire you, no matter where you are in the world. Remember, many of the recipes found in the quick bites, big bowls and sides chapters can be made into main events, too.

- Red Lentil Coconut Curry
- Almond Mung Bean Burgers with Sweet French Fries
- Old-School Macro Plate
- Lasagne
- Sourdough Pizza
- Cornbread, Beans and Greens
- Barley Risotto with Shiitake and Sweet White Miso
- Marlene's Vegan Paella
- Sizzling Jaja Tofu
- Vegetable Pad Thai in Tamarind Sauce
- Rice and Bean Enchiladas
- Teriyaki Black Bean Burgers
- Portobello Mushroom Stroganoff
- Saffron-Scented Vegetable Tagine on a Bed of Herbed Couscous
- Vegetable and Tempeh Wellington with Shiitake Gravy
- Roasted Red Pepper and Chickpea Korma
- Tricolour Quinoa Vegetable Stir-Fry with Teriyaki Sauce
- Spaghetti with Basil and Watercress Pesto
- Vegan Shepherd's Pie with Shiitake Gravy

Red Lentil Coconut Curry

This warming curry in the South Indian style is flavoured with aromatic fresh ginger, cumin and coriander. It's made extra creamy and luscious thanks to the addition of organic coconut cream. Serve the curry with white or brown basmati rice to round out this comforting meal.

3 shallots, finely chopped
1 tbsp fresh ginger, peeled and minced
2 cloves garlic, minced
1 tsp cumin seeds
1 tsp mild curry powder
½ tsp ground coriander
½ tsp turmeric
Pinch sea salt
2 cups filtered water
1½ cups red lentils
1 cup organic coconut cream
2 medium-sized courgettes, diced into ½ inch (1 cm) pieces
1 or 2 tbsp tamari
1 cup loosely packed fresh coriander leaves, chopped
Lime slices

In a heavy-based pan, cook the shallots, ginger and garlic in a splash of filtered water for 5 minutes, stirring occasionally. Add the spices and salt and stir well. Stir in the water, lentils and coconut cream. Allow the mixture to simmer over a low flame, covered, whilst stirring occasionally for 10 minutes. Stir in the courgette and tamari, cover and cook until courgette and lentils are tender. Add more water to reach the desired consistency. Taste-test then stir in the coriander. Makes 4–6 servings.

Almond Mung Bean Burgers with Sweet French Fries

Mung beans, a type of small, green legume in the same plant family as peas and lentils, are a high source of protein, fibre, antioxidants and phytonutrients. Mung beans quickly sprout thick, white, crisp shoots and are a popular source of beansprouts. Apart from making mung bean soup and sprouting my mung beans 365 days a year, I use them to make these burgers. This is one of the most economical recipes you can create at home.

2 cups mung beans
2 inch (5 cm) piece of kombu seaweed
3 cloves garlic
2 red onions, finely diced
1 tbsp mixed herbs
1 tsp onion powder
1 tsp paprika
½ tsp garlic granules
1 instant umami stock sachet dissolved in 2 tbsp hot filtered water
1 cup ground almonds
1 cup cooked short-grain brown rice
½ cup sesame seeds
3 carrots, grated
1 courgette, grated
½ cup sweet roasted red pepper, finely diced

Optional toppings

Oil-free mayonnaise (page 194)
Balsamic glaze

Soak the mung beans and kombu seaweed in filtered water overnight. Rinse well and soak overnight once again. Drain and rinse, discarding the soaking water. The beans will expand and start to open; they are now ready to use. Soaking the beans with kombu seaweed further activates enzymes helpful for digestion (this is true for all legumes). Preheat the oven to 200°C (400°F), gas 6. Place the mung beans, garlic, onion, herbs, seasoning and umami stock mixture into a food processor. Process (on pulse) until the mixture looks semi-smooth but not creamy. Transfer to a large bowl and add the ground almonds, rice and sesame seeds. Fold in the carrots, courgettes and sweet red pepper. If the mixture seems too wet, add some more ground almonds.

Note – The mixture will dry out when baked so you are looking for a 'moist' mixture and not one that is dry and dense. Take a heaped tablespoon of the mixture and shape into a burger

(continued)

using your hands or a burger press. Place the burgers onto a parchment-lined baking sheet. Bake for 20–25 minutes, flipping over after 15 minutes of cooking. Deliciously crisp on the outside and soft and succulent on the inside. Serve with some of my vegan mayo and top with some balsamic glaze. Makes 24 burgers.

Sweet French fries

  Sweet potatoes
  Sea salt
  Dried thyme or rosemary

Peel the potatoes, top and tail them so you have blunt ends, then slice them into equal-sized pieces. Sweet potatoes are faster to cook than potatoes, so I cut mine into 1 inch (2 cm) pieces, so they don't burn. Place the slices into a large bowl and sprinkle with some refined sea salt and herbs. Use your hands and mix to massage the chips. Lay them out in a single layer on a parchment-lined roasting tin and cover with a baking sheet. Place in a cold oven to allow the sugars to be released slowly. Bake at 200°C (400°F), gas 6, for 25 minutes. Remove the cover, flip over and bake 10 minutes more. uncovered. I often add a splash or two of water to the roasting tin at this stage, so the fries don't dry out. This is one of my favourite snacks, hot or cold, I love them.

Note – For perfectly crisp crisps (chips, in the US) cut into ¼ inch or thinner round slices. It's easy to do this in a more uniform fashion with a mandolin. Cook them for less time, around 10 minutes either side. Once cooked, allow them to cool to crisp up.

Old-School Macro Plate

We love and live on grains and beans with lots of seasonal vegetables. Variety is the spice of life, as the saying goes. However, variety in the vast array of beans and grains offers so much choice and versatility you can create amazing breakfasts, lunches and dinners within these three food groups.

Replicate my plate

Short-grain brown rice
Sweet kidney beans
Lemon-scented arame sauté (page 173)
Red radish slices
Blanched greens, carrots and mange tout
Sautéed pak choi (bok choi) with garlic and ginger
Lemon and lime tahini sauce
(pages 191–192)

To cook the rice in a pressure cooker

Wash and rinse two cups of short-grain brown rice in a sieve. Soak in 4 cups of filtered water, for a minimum of 1 hour or preferably overnight. Transfer to a pressure cooker and add a pinch of sea salt. Bring to full pressure, place a flame spreader under the pressure cooker and cook on low for 25 minutes. Allow the pressure to come down on its own, around 20 minutes.

To cook the beans

1 cup dried kidney beans
2 inch (5 cm) piece of kombu

Cover the beans in filtered water and soak overnight. Discard the soaking water, transfer the beans and kombu to a pressure cooker and cover with water, about 2 inches (5 cm) above the beans. Pressure-cook for 30 minutes. Remove from the heat and allow the pressure to release naturally.

To make the bean mixture

2 cups cooked kidney beans
1 medium onion, chopped
1½ cups Romano yellow, orange and red sweet bell pepper, chopped
3 stalks celery, chopped
Pinch sea salt
3 cloves garlic, minced
2 bay leaves
1 tsp dried thyme
4 cups umami stock

Warm a splash or two of stock or filtered water in a heavy-based pan. Add the onion, pepper, celery and salt. Cook, stirring frequently, until the onions and celery are semi-translucent, and the peppers are tender, 6 to 8 minutes. Add the garlic and cook for 1 to 2 minutes, stirring constantly. Add the bay leaves, thyme, umami stock and beans to the pot and increase the heat to high. Cook, stirring frequently until the mixture comes to a boil, approximately 6 to 8 minutes. Decrease the heat to maintain a simmer, cover and cook for 10–15 minutes.

Blanched greens, carrots and mange tout

1 cup carrots, sliced on the diagonal
1 small bunch kale, destemmed and torn into pieces
1 small pack mange tout

(continued)

Bring a pot of filtered water to the boil. Place the carrots, kale and mange tout in the water for 1–2 minutes. Drain and rinse under cold running water. Set aside.

Sautéed pak choi (bok choi) with garlic and ginger

2 cloves garlic, minced
1 tbsp fresh ginger, minced
2 heads of pak choi, thoroughly cleaned
¼ cup stock or filtered water
1 tsp tamari or shoyu
Toasted sesame seeds

Chop the stems into ½ inch (1 cm) slices, preferably on the diagonal, up to where the leaves start. The leaves are kept whole unless they are large, in which case they're cut in half. Warm a splash or two of filtered water in a large sauté pan over medium-high heat and add the ginger and garlic, along with the stems of the pak choi. Stir for a couple of minutes. Add a few tablespoons of stock or water and allow it to cook off as the stems soften.

Add the choi leaves and tips together to the pan. The leaves will cook down fairly rapidly, so there will be room to add more. Using tongs, stir and turn the choi leaves to cook for a minute. Add a few more tablespoons of stock or water along with the tamari and stir well. Continue tossing the choi as it cooks to the desired consistency of soft, bright

green leaves and tender stems, neither should be mushy (should only take a few minutes), then turn off the heat. Serve with a sprinkle of toasted sesame seeds.

Assembling

Create your own plate, or follow my image here. Makes 4–6 servings.

Note – You can also assemble this plate from leftover grains and beans, arame, and pickles. Simply cook the vegetables fresh.

The winter season has challenges for most people who live in a four-season climate. Depending on where you live, the main challenge is keeping warm. It seems also that our body clock wants to slow down in the winter and get more rest, even more sleep. This is not always possible living a modern life, but it is important to be aware of, and do our best to reduce stress. Heart attacks spike in the winter months (even without the usual snow-shovelling reasons). There is also a rise in seasonal affective disorder, especially in areas where sunny periods are few. The coldness coupled with a lack of sunshine produces anxiety and depression. In Chinese medicine, this time of year was seen to be a season where kidney health was of utmost importance. Eating warming stews, and particularly beans, is nourishing. It is a good idea to make sure the lower back area is kept warm. Using sea vegetables to assure a good range of trace minerals is also helpful.

Lasagne

The best vegan lasagne is the one you make at home! I use brown rice organic lasagne sheets that do not require precooking. This super-healthy vegan lasagne is hearty, filled with vegetables, and so good! The rich tomato sauce layered with a creamy mushroom and spinach filling is seriously savoury and satisfying.

Sauce

4 cups Marlene's basic tomato sauce (pages 192–193)

Vegetable filling

1 pack silken tofu
½ tsp turmeric
2 tsp umeboshi paste
3 cloves garlic, minced
1 cup spring onions, sliced
3 cups fresh button or chestnut mushrooms, thinly sliced
Pinch sea salt
½ tsp onion granules
2 tbsp shoyu or tamari
2 cups courgette, thinly sliced
1 tsp oregano
1 tsp basil
3 cups spinach
2 tbsp nutritional yeast

Topping

Vegan parmesan or nut-based vegan cheese

Vegan parmesan

This vegan substitute for parmesan cheese contains no processed ingredients. It's perfect for shaking over pastas, soups and stews.

½ cup ground almonds
½ cup organic nutritional yeast
Dash of onion powder
Dash of sea salt

Put the ingredients into a condiment shaker, shake well to mix. Store in the refrigerator.

Preheat the oven to 180°C (350°F), gas 4. Drain the tofu of excess water, crumble into a bowl, and stir in the turmeric and umeboshi paste. Set aside. Place the courgette slices on a parchment-lined baking sheet. Sprinkle with some sea salt and drizzle a little balsamic vinegar over. Roast for 20 minutes, turning over halfway. Remove and set aside.

Warm a splash or two of filtered water in a heavy-based sauté pan, add the garlic, spring onions, mushrooms, sea salt, onion granules, and shoyu or tamari. Sauté over a medium heat for 5 minutes; cover between stirring. Add a little water to keep the mixture from drying out. Stir in the oregano, basil and spinach. Place the lid back on the pan and continue cooking for a few more minutes until the spinach is wilted. Remove from the heat and season with some ground black pepper if desired. Set aside and let cool. Transfer the vegetable mixture to the tofu bowl and mix well. Stir in the roasted courgette slices.

Assembling

Spread a thin layer of tomato sauce in the bottom of the baking dish. Place a layer of lasagne sheets over the sauce, spread

(continued)

more sauce and some filling. Cover with another layer of noodles. Again, top with some more sauce and the remainder of the filling. Add a final layer of noodles and cover with the remaining sauce. Sprinkle with vegan parmesan or nut-based vegan cheese. Cover the dish tightly with a lid. Bake for 25 minutes at 180°C. Remove the lid and bake for another 20 minutes. Leave to cool for 10 minutes. Makes 6 servings. Freezes well also.

Optional – Vary the dish by changing the vegetables or adding some crumbled tempeh. Simply sauté the tempeh along with the vegetable mixture.

Many 'vegan options' are filled with chemical additives and excess salt. They are commonly touted as being protein-rich, but often contain TSP (texturised soya protein; also known as textured vegetable protein, or TVP), excessive sugars and salt, and are expensive in the long run. Eating a plant-based vegan diet does not mean living on processed foods, sweets or sugary drinks. Your best health choices are to eat 'food as grown'. Corn on the cob is quite different from corn chips; potatoes are a wholefood, but potato crisps are not. Ready-made vegan foods are becoming more available and are quick to use and sometimes helpful when you're rushed for time. Read the ingredients well before using. To get the greatest benefit from your foods, the simpler the better. Eating imitation meats and burgers may be fine as an occasional time-saver, but is not the answer to a healthy diet.

Sourdough Pizza

Making your own sourdough pizza crust is not for everyone, but it will bring your pizza to a higher level. Sourdough produces a pizza crust which is slightly fluffier and chewier. Bill has mastered the best sourdough crust I have ever tasted. He did, however, have first-hand experience, having lived in San Francisco for many years (next to a bakery, may I add). We enjoy a pizza every so often and it's fun to do when friends come over – we make them work for their supper! Vary your toppings on each one or make the four pizzas the same. In the pizza shown we used thinly sliced mushrooms, red onion, thinly sliced grilled artichoke hearts and black olives. After baking I garnish with some fresh rocket/arugula and basil. Of course, you can purchase ready-made pizza crusts, but there are many people who have asked me for a home-made recipe to try, so here it is.

How do you make sourdough pizza crust?

The starter for your sourdough is available through bakeries and online. They will indicate how to feed the starter to get you started.

In this recipe there are four basic steps:

1. Creating the sponge and allowing it to develop
2. Mixing and kneading the dough and letting it rise (also known as bulk fermentation)
3. Rolling the dough out, adding the sauce and toppings
4. Baking the pizza in the oven.

You only require about 45 minutes of active time to prepare your dough and then to create and bake the pizza.

Measurements by weight
Sponge
250 g (9 oz) sourdough starter (active and hungry)
310 g (10 oz) filtered water
340 g (12 oz) unbleached wheat flour

Bulk fermentation
½ tbsp sea salt
330 g (12 oz) unbleached wheat flour

To make the sponge

Pour the sourdough starter into a large bowl. Add the water and flour. Mix together gently with a wooden spoon. Cover the bowl with a cheesecloth or a dish towel. Leave the covered bowl in a place sheltered from drafts for 6 to 12 hours. After this period of resting, you will have a sponge (a frothy mix, with bubbles on top). The bubbles show the sponge is active.

Bulk fermentation

Add the amount of flour and salt indicated for the bulk fermentation stage into the bowl with the sponge. Mix together with a wooden spoon. Let it sit for a few minutes. Continue mixing with a spoon until the dough starts coming together. Turn the dough out onto a clean floured board or hard surface. Knead for about 5 minutes. If the dough is sticky, add a little more flour; if dry, add a few drops of water. The dough should not stick to your hands when you knead it.

(continued)

Divide into four parts. Place each piece in a bowl with enough space for the dough to double. Cover each bowl with a cheesecloth or clean dish towel. Let the dough sit for about 6 hours, until it has more or less doubled. The skin of the dough may start to feel a little dry or the top may begin to crack.

Stretching the dough

Preheat the oven to 220°C (450°F), gas 8, with your pizza stone or pizza pan inside. I use a pizza stone, with great results. Let it heat for at least 10 minutes. Place parchment paper on a flat surface. Sprinkle flour on the parchment paper so the dough will not stick.

Gently pick up one of the parts of dough and roll it into a ball. Put the ball on the floured parchment paper. Flatten it down. Place your hand on the dough and start stretching the dough by pushing outward from the centre of the ball with the heel of your hand, to form a disk. Continue gently stretching while being careful not to stretch it too thin or to make holes.

Use a fork to poke holes in the pizza dough. Spread your tomato sauce on top of the pizza, leaving the edges bare. Use Marlene's basic tomato sauce (pages 192–193) or use shop-bought tomato sauce. Be careful not to put on too much sauce or your pizza will become soggy. Add vegan parmesan on top

(*continued*)

of your pizza, then add your other toppings. Do not overload the pizza or the dough may not support all the toppings.

Let the prepared pizza sit for 5 to 10 minutes, then place it in the oven. Let it bake for about 10 minutes, or until the crust turns golden brown and the toppings look cooked. Remove it from the oven and let it sit for a couple of minutes before slicing it. This recipe makes 4 pizzas.

Note – When making the sponge, you can use a blend of flours. For this pizza crust, I mixed one-half unbleached bread flour and one-half plain flour.

Note that you will add flour at two stages: the sponge and the bulk fermentation stages. You can leave the dough in the refrigerator for up to five days during the bulk fermentation stage. However, take care to cover it well so it does not dry out and become crusty.

 Barry Commoner, the father of modern ecological studies, pointed out that there is 'no free lunch'. Whatever we do in our relationship to planet earth we must pay for. This is the law of karma – cause and effect. When we treat the environment poorly it invariably causes economic chaos and illness. Consider the issue of zoonoses, diseases that begin in one species and spread to another. In recent history the unsanitary, unhealthy conditions for farm animals have contributed to these diseases. Many health professionals are worried about future health problems caused by disorders that arise in this way. Diseases that originated in animals and have transferred to humans include bird flu, swine flu, Ebola, mad cow disease and HIV. Using animals for food simply to satisfy our pleasure is a moral tragedy and a dangerous threat to our lives.

Cornbread, Greens and Beans

'Soup beans' is a term common in the southern United States. This is my version of the American classic. Soup beans are usually served with cornbread and greens (such as boiled cabbage, cauliflower or sauerkraut). Soup beans are considered a main course, but also serve as a side dish. In rural areas, where food was scarce during the winter, these dried beans were a staple food. I always cook up way more than I need when pressure-cooking beans, to have cooked beans in the freezer. I simply take them out the night before I need them, and suggest you get into the habit of doing this too.

Cornbread
    1 cup cornmeal
    1 cup soy milk
    ½ cup plain flour, gluten free if preferred
    ½ cup ground almonds (almond flour)
    ¼ cup maple syrup
    2 tsp baking powder
    ¼ tsp sea salt

Preheat the oven to 180°C (350°F), gas 4. Whisk together the dry ingredients. In a separate bowl, whisk the wet ingredients. Mix both together (do not overmix). Pour into an 8 × 8 inch baking dish and bake for approximately 25 minutes, or until a toothpick comes out clean.

Greens
Greens, rich in chlorophyll and minerals like calcium, strengthen the bones, help the blood to absorb oxygen and bring energy upward in the body, leaving you feeling light and refreshed. Because greens have absorbed so much light, they are like 'eating sunshine'.

    1 large bunch fresh spring greens, kale or
        collards
    Balsamic glaze

Wash the greens, and separate the green leaf from the tough stem by slicing carefully along each side of the stem. Slice or tear the leaves into bite-sized pieces and place in a steamer basket. Bring a small amount of filtered water to a boil. Add the steamer basket with the greens, cover and steam for 4–5 minutes. The greens will go from their raw colour to a very brilliant green, then a deeper green. Drizzle with a little balsamic glaze before serving.

To pressure-cook the beans
    1 cup dried pinto beans
    Small piece kombu

Add the pinto beans and kombu to a large bowl and cover with filtered water. Soak overnight. Drain the water and place the beans and kombu in a pressure cooker. Add the water to about 2 inches (5 cm) above the beans. Bring to full pressure then reduce heat and cook for 30 minutes. Allow the pressure to come down naturally.

To make the bean mixture
    3 cups cooked pinto beans
    1 onion, diced
    3 large cloves garlic, minced
    Pinch sea salt

(continued)

½ cup sun-dried tomatoes, diced

1 umami instant stock sachet dissolved in 2 cups warm filtered water

¼ tsp each of cumin, garlic granules, oregano, coriander, paprika, ground cinnamon

1 tbsp tamari or shoyu

½ cup fresh coriander, chopped

To serve

Lime slices

Sour cream (pages 185–186)

Apple sauce (page 196)

In a large pot, warm a splash or two of filtered water over a medium heat. Add the diced onion, garlic, and pinch of sea salt. Sauté for 3–4 minutes, or until the onion is soft and translucent. Add the cooked beans, tomatoes, umami stock and seasonings. Bring to a boil, then cover and reduce to a simmer for 20 minutes. Stir in the tamari and fresh coriander. Serve with some cornbread and greens, a hefty dollop of sour cream, and a slice of fresh lime, and if desired some apple sauce on the side. Makes 4–6 servings.

Barley Risotto with Shiitake and Sweet White Miso

Love risotto? Try this low-fat version, which swaps pearl barley for the traditional risotto rice. Pearl barley is much cheaper than traditional risotto rice and more flavoursome too.

1 cup organic pearl barley
1 sachet umami instant stock
4 cups hot filtered water
4 cloves fresh garlic, minced
1 tsp fresh ginger, minced
2 cups spring onions, thinly sliced
2 cups fresh shiitake mushrooms, thinly sliced
Pinch sea salt
1 tsp dried Italian seasoning
1 cup fresh green peas
2 tbsp sweet white miso
2 tbsp nutritional yeast
Balsamic vinegar glaze
Spring onions

Dissolve the umami stock in the water and set aside. Heat a splash or two of filtered water in a heavy-based pan. Add the garlic, ginger, spring onions and mushrooms, along with the sea salt and seasoning. Sauté for 5 minutes. Add the barley and 1 cup of the stock. Bring to a slow boil, then cover and reduce heat to low. As the liquid absorbs, continue to add one cup at a time until the stock is used up. The pearl barley will be soft and swollen when cooked, which takes approximately 30 minutes. Stir in the green peas, sweet white miso and nutritional yeast. Turn off the heat. Let stand 2–3 minutes to cool. Ladle into warmed bowls and drizzle with the balsamic vinegar. Garnish with spring onions. Makes 4–6 servings.

Marlene's Vegan Paella

Food has a very powerful influence on our physical, mental, emotional and spiritual well-being. A macrobiotic vegan approach to diet is the most helpful to create delicious balanced meals. Enjoy my version of the typical Spanish paella.

½ tsp saffron threads
2 cloves garlic, crushed
1 onion, finely chopped
2 shallots, finely chopped
2 tomatoes, finely chopped
1 red pepper, 1 yellow pepper and 1 green pepper, deseeded and finely chopped
1 sachet umami instant stock mixed in 2 cups hot filtered water
2 tbsp tamari or shoyu
2 cups paella rice
1 cup frozen green peas
1 tbsp lemon juice
Lemon wedges
Fresh basil

Soak the saffron threads in two cups of filtered water and set to one side. In a large paella pan, heat a splash of filtered water and add the garlic, onion, shallots and tomatoes. Sauté over a low heat until soft. Add the peppers and cover with the umami stock. Add the tamari and leave to cook on a low heat for 15 minutes, until the vegetables are al dente, soft to the bite, adding more water if necessary. Add the rice and the saffron threads with the soaking water, adding additional water if required. Simmer covered for 20–25 minutes, until the rice is soft to the bite. Stir in the peas and lemon juice. Allow to sit for 5 minutes. Serve with lemon wedges and fresh basil leaves. Makes 4–6 servings.

Sizzling JaJa Tofu

This is an easy-to-cook tofu dish. I recommend using extra-firm tofu for this recipe in order to get the best result. Can be served not only as a 'main event' but also as an appetiser or side dish.

300 g pack tofu, cut into 8 equal slices
1 tbsp ginger-flavoured umami paste
1 clove garlic, crushed
2 small shallots, thinly sliced
1 small red onion, thinly sliced
1 carrot, cut into thin strips
2 cups sugar snap peas
2 tbsp mirin
2 tbsp shoyu
1 tbsp juice from freshly grated ginger
½ cup bean sprouts
1–2 tsp brown rice syrup
Spring onions for garnish

Warm a heavy-based pan and sauté the garlic, shallots and red onion in the umami paste and a little filtered water. Add the carrot and sugar snap peas and a splash or two of shoyu, cover and cook for 2–3 minutes. Remove from the pan and set aside. Place the tofu slices into the pan and add the mirin, shoyu and grated ginger juice, with a splash or two of filtered water. Cook 5–7 minutes each side. Warm the sizzle plate on a burner for 5 minutes. Meanwhile, add the bean sprouts to the tofu pan and mix through the tofu. Drizzle a little brown rice syrup over the tofu for the last two minutes of cooking. Transfer the sautéed vegetables to the sizzle plate, top with the tofu and serve immediately with your choice of noodles, grain and vegetables. Garnish with spring onions. Makes 4 servings.

Vegetable Pad Thai in Tamarind Sauce

This pad thai recipe is full of only the best unrefined, healthy and nourishing ingredients. Tamarind tastes a bit like a date but is less sweet (and more sour), and is sometimes known as the Indian date. It is a key ingredient in Worcestershire sauce.

    1 pack brown rice or udon noodles
    1 cup bean sprouts
    2 large garlic cloves, finely minced
    ½ large red onion, finely chopped
    1 carrot, cut into fine matchsticks
    ½ cup spring onions, thinly sliced
    ¼ cup fresh mint leaves, chopped
    ¼ cup fresh basil leaves, chopped

Garnish

    ½ cup toasted sunflower and pumpkin seeds
    ¼ cup red radish, very thinly sliced
    Fresh lime slices

Tamarind sauce

    2 tbsp tamarind paste
    2 tbsp brown rice vinegar
    1½ tbsp shoyu
    1½ tbsp rice mirin
    1 tbsp ume plum seasoning
    1 tbsp freshly squeezed ginger juice
    4 tbsp maple syrup

Cook the noodles according to the packet instructions and set aside. Add the tamarind sauce ingredients to a small pan. Bring to a boil and then simmer on a very low heat for 1 minute. Remove from the heat and set aside. Heat a splash of filtered water in a wok over a high heat and add the garlic, onion, carrot and spring onions, with a pinch of sea salt. Mix together and cook for 3–4 minutes. Add the noodles, tamarind sauce, bean sprouts and herbs. Stir to combine and turn off the heat. Add the radish slices and seeds on top.

To serve – Add some·more fresh herbs, freshly grated carrot, bean sprouts, lime, radish slices and some nuts of your choice. If you desire a hot sensation you can serve with pickled chillies on the side.

Note – Deseed and finely slice chillies and add them to a bowl with the juice of 1½ limes and ½ tsp of maple syrup. Leave aside to pickle. Makes 4–6 servings.

Rice and Bean Enchiladas

I have been making this recipe with many variations for decades. It's simple and delicious and has all the ingredients for a power-packed lunch or dinner. When we have friends over, I serve it with some guacamole (page 188) and corn chips alongside.

For the rice

    1 cup red wild rice
    2½ cups filtered water
    Pinch sea salt

The vegetable and bean mixture

    1 onion, diced
    5 cloves garlic, minced
    1 tsp ground coriander
    2 tsp ground cumin
    2 cups fresh spinach, chopped
    2 cups cooked black (turtle) beans,
        mashed
    2 tbsp tamari
    3 cups cooked sweet potatoes, mashed
    Sea salt, to taste

To serve

    10 large corn tortillas
    Salsa (pages 187–188)
    Vegan parmesan (see lasagne recipe,
        pages 114–116)
    Finely diced spring onion for garnish

To cook the beans

    1 cup dried black (turtle) beans
    2 inch (5 cm) piece of kombu

Soak the beans overnight in 3 cups of filtered water. Drain, rinse and discard the soaking water. Place the beans, kombu and enough filtered water to come 1 inch (2 cm) above the beans in a heavy-based pot. Bring to a boil, skimming off the white foam as it arises on the surface. Place a flame spreader under the pot, cover and reduce heat to medium low. Simmer for around 45 minutes, or until beans are tender. Check the liquid during cooking, adding more water if necessary, to cover the beans.

Use the required amount of cooked beans, and refrigerate or freeze any leftover beans.

To cook the rice

Rinse the rice and place in a large bowl or pot. Add enough filtered water to cover, and soak for 30 minutes. Drain the rice and place in a heavy-based pot with the filtered water and a pinch of sea salt. Bring to a boil, reduce to a low flame, cover and simmer until rice is soft and cooked through, about 20–25 minutes. Fluff before serving.

To cook the sweet potato mash

Bring a large pot of filtered water to a rolling boil. Peel the sweet potatoes and cut into chunks. Add to the pot with a pinch of sea salt. Cover and cook for 15 minutes. Remove from the heat, drain and mash with a potato masher.

Preheat the oven to 180°C (350°F), gas 4.

(continued)

To make the vegetable filling

Heat a splash of filtered water in a heavy-based pan over a low-medium heat. Add the onion and garlic, and sauté until the onion is translucent. Add the coriander and cumin. Cook for two minutes, stirring constantly, adding a little water if the pan seems dry. Add the spinach, black beans, tamari and mashed sweet potatoes. Cook for 3–5 minutes. Remove from heat.

Assembling

Place ¼ cup of mixture in the centre of a corn tortilla and top with a layer of the red rice. Roll into a burrito and close by placing a toothpick into the centre of the tortilla. Transfer to a parchment-lined baking tray. Once all the burritos are assembled, pour your favourite salsa on top and sprinkle with vegan parmesan. Cover and bake for 25 minutes. Served warm, garnished with spring onions. Makes 10 enchiladas.

Note – You can purchase organic cooked black beans for quickness. I always cook up double or triple the amount of black beans I need, and store the rest in the freezer.

Teriyaki Black Bean Burgers

Vegan burgers can be made with chickpeas, black beans, white beans, potatoes, lentils and pretty much any other vegetable that can be mashed and formed into a burger.

    2 cups cooked black beans or mixed
        beans (instructions in enchiladas
        recipe, pages 132–134)
    1 cup cooked short-grain brown rice
        (instructions in introduction to big
        bowls chapter, page 89)
    1 cup silken tofu
    2 heaped tbsp mild salsa
    1 tbsp lime zest
    1 red onion, chopped
    2–3 garlic cloves, minced
    1 tsp ground coriander
    1 tsp dried oregano
    1 tsp smoked paprika
    1 tbsp teriyaki sauce
    ½ cup fresh coriander, minced
    1 cup sourdough breadcrumbs
    Oil-free mayonnaise for serving (page 194)

Note – For kids I would suggest using regular paprika – no spices.

To make the sourdough breadcrumbs

    8 slices stale sourdough bread, torn into
        1 inch (2 cm) pieces
    1 tbsp Italian seasoning
    ½ tsp garlic powder
    ¼ tsp sea salt

Preheat the oven to 170°C (340°F), gas 3. Place all of the ingredients into a food processor and pulse until coarse crumbs form. Spread the crumbs evenly on two parchment-lined baking sheets. Bake until they just begin to brown and are crisp, about 5 minutes. Cool the crumbs on the baking sheets for 20 minutes, and then transfer to an airtight container and store at room temperature for up to 2 weeks.

To make the burgers

Preheat the oven to 180° (350°), gas 4. Line two baking trays with parchment paper. In a large bowl, mash the beans with a fork or potato masher. Add the cooked rice, tofu, salsa and lime zest, and mix well. Warm a splash or two of filtered water in a small pan and sauté the red onion, garlic, dried herbs, paprika and teriyaki for 5–7 minutes. Add this mixture to the bowl and stir to combine. Fold in the fresh coriander and breadcrumbs. Take a heaped tablespoon of the mixture and squeeze together with your hands to form a burger. If not cohesive enough, add some more breadcrumbs. Place on the baking trays and cook the burgers in the middle of the oven for 25 minutes, turning once halfway through. Makes 8 good-sized burgers. Double or triple the quantities and freeze for quick lunch/dinner options.

Note – For consistent thickness and shape that cooks evenly and won't fall apart if you are grilling the burgers, I use my three-in-one gourmet burger press. Just add your ingredients to this patty maker and press. The non-stick bottom pops up so you can remove your perfectly round, bun-sized

(*continued*)

burgers with ease and without mess. Cook the burgers on a hot grill for 4 to 5 minutes on each side, until crisp and golden. They will 'blacken' slightly because of the beans. Serve with a selection of crisp salad greens, fresh sprouts and radishes. Garnish with snipped chives.

Note – My sweet potato fries accompanying these burgers on toasted sourdough with fresh salad leaves, sliced red onion and sprouts are a favourite with everyone. Top with cucumber, pickles and your favourite salsa.

 In the spring, vegetal energy begins to move upward from the root systems toward the leaves. Many of the vegetables that grow at this time of year were prized for their cleansing qualities. In China this rising energy was called **tree energy**. The associated organs were the liver and the gall bladder. If a person had eaten more heavy foods, especially oily or fatty foods, during the winter months, the liver could be gently relaxed by eating the sprouts from barley and other plants. In my kitchen we use sprouted grains and beans on a daily basis. Our sprouting dishes are always at work growing sprouted seeds, grains or beans to use as a garnish on all our meals.

Portobello Mushroom Stroganoff

A vegan mushroom stroganoff that's as rich and delicious as its meaty counterpart. I have even converted beef and dairy farmers to veganism after they tasted my stroganoff. Now that did make my heart sing.

For the sauce

1 cup cashews, soaked overnight
1½ cups filtered water
1 tbsp ume plum vinegar
1 heaped tbsp tahini
1 tbsp tamari or shoyu

For the stroganoff

3 cups portobello mushrooms, very thinly sliced
1 large onion, thinly sliced
1 shallot, thinly sliced
2 cloves garlic, minced
1 umami instant stock sachet dissolved in 2 cups warm filtered water
1 tbsp Italian seasoning
½ cup tightly packed fresh parsley, chopped

Garnish

Black sesame seeds
Chopped coriander
Lemon zest

Warm a splash or two of filtered water in a heavy-based pot on a medium-low flame. Sauté the mushrooms, onion, shallot and garlic for 5 minutes. Reduce the heat to low and add the umami stock and the Italian seasoning. Cover and simmer for 15 minutes.

Drain the cashews from their soaking water and place in a blender with the remaining sauce ingredients. Blend to a cream. Add this cashew cream to the pot mixture, stirring well to combine. Cook, covered, on a low simmer for 15 minutes. Add water to reach the desired consistency.

The stroganoff will thicken as it sits, so make sure to thin slightly before serving. Stir in the chopped parsley. Delicious served on a bed of fluffy basmati rice. Serve in bowls, garnished with black sesame seeds, chopped coriander and lemon zest. Makes 4–6 servings.

Lime- and coriander-scented fluffy basmati rice

2 cups organic basmati rice
3 cups boiling filtered water
Pinch sea salt
Freshly squeezed juice of 1 small lime
½ cup tightly packed coriander, minced

Using a strainer, rinse the rice under cold running water. Soak in a large bowl of filtered water for 1 hour. Drain and transfer to a heavy-based pot and add the salt. Pour 3 cups of boiling water over the rice. When the water starts boiling and steaming, cover the pot tightly with a heavy lid so that no steam escapes. Turn down the heat to just above its lowest setting and let the rice cook for 15 minutes undisturbed. I like to use my flame spreader for even heat distribution. After 15 minutes, remove the pot from the heat. Allow the rice to steam another 10 minutes before removing the lid. Transfer to a large bowl and fold in the coriander and lime juice. Fluff the rice and serve.

Saffron-Scented Vegetable Tagine on a Bed of Herbed Couscous

An exotic warm stew that is very easy to make. The saffron lends a wonderful flavour and brilliant yellow colour to this potassium-rich dish. A pungent blend of different spices makes a wonderful autumnal tagine packed with flavour. When made the day before, the flavours infuse further to make this a showstopper to woo your guests with.

2 cloves garlic, crushed
1 large red onion, diced
2 cloves garlic, minced
1 tsp ground cumin
1 tsp ground coriander
2 cups cooked organic chickpeas (see classic hummus recipe, pages 186–187)
½ cup dehydrated tomatoes, chopped small
2 tbsp tomato passata
¼ tsp saffron threads, soaked in ½ cup filtered water
1 carrot, cut into small dice
1 small sweet potato, peeled and cut into small dice
1 celery stick, thinly sliced
2 cinnamon sticks
1 sachet umami instant stock or 2 vegetable stock cubes dissolved in 6 cups hot filtered water
2 cups fresh shiitake or button mushrooms, washed and thinly sliced
12 dried unsulphured apricots, thinly sliced
¼ cup each fresh parsley and coriander

Garnish
Fresh mint
Pomegranate seeds
Meyer lemons

Soak the saffron threads for 30 minutes before using. Heat a splash or two of filtered water in a heavy-based pan. Add the garlic, onion and spices. Heat on low for 5 minutes, stirring to coat the vegetables with the spices. Add the chickpeas, tomatoes, tomato passata, saffron threads (and soaking water), carrot, sweet potato, celery, cinnamon sticks and stock. Bring to a boil, and simmer on a low heat for 20 minutes. Add the dried apricots and mushrooms and continue to simmer for another 25–30 minutes, adding more liquid if required. Stir in the fresh parsley and coriander and serve with some herbed couscous and fresh salad greens. Garnish with fresh mint, pomegranate seeds and lemon segments.

Herbed couscous
3 cups couscous
4½ cups boiling filtered water
Pinch sea salt
1 tsp herbs de Provence
½ cup toasted flaked almonds

Spread the couscous evenly in the bottom of a large casserole so that it is in as thin a layer as possible. Add the salt and herbs to the boiling water and gently pour over the couscous. Cover tightly with a lid or

(continued)

compostable cling film. Set aside for about 15 minutes, then fluff with a fork and mix through the flaked almonds. Makes 6–8 servings.

Note – Meyer lemons don't have the same tang as regular lemons. Instead, they're much sweeter, so much so that some people enjoy adding the raw segments to their salads or desserts. Their rinds also have a more complex scent than regular lemons, a spicy bergamot fragrance that tastes and smells more like a herb or a spice, and works well with this North African favourite dish.

Note – The difference between orange and brown dried apricots is to do with sulphur. Sulphur dioxide prevents dried fruit from spoiling. It's often used for brightly coloured fruit to keep them more attractive. Some of the most commonly sulphured fruits are dried apricots, peaches, apples, pineapple, papaya, mango and golden raisins. The dried fruit contains only very small amounts of sulphur dioxide, which are well below recognised toxic amounts! Despite this fact, there is reason to be cautious about eating sulphured fruit. Sulphur dioxide can induce asthma when inhaled or ingested by those who are sensitive to it, even in small amounts.

Vegetable and Tempeh Wellington with Shiitake Gravy

This recipe may take a bit of preparation but it's well worth it. Rather than making your own pastry, a short cut option that I offer here is to purchase an organic vegan pastry from the frozen section of your natural food store. With a plethora of roasted root vegetables, creamy mashed potatoes and gravy, it's our go-to festive meal. I would recommend making the vegan egg wash before assembling the wellington.

250 g pack vegan puff pastry
225 g pack organic tempeh, cubed and marinated
1 bunch spinach, chopped
6 medium portobello mushrooms, sliced ¼ inch thick
Pinch sea salt
2 tbsp red wine
2 cloves garlic, minced
2 large leeks, white part only, trimmed and cut into ½ inch slices
2 cups celery, thinly sliced
2 cups red onion, thinly sliced
2 cups carrots, thinly sliced
1 tbsp tamari
½ tsp dried sage
½ tsp dried thyme
1 large carrot, thinly cut on the diagonal and steamed
Basil and watercress pesto (page 191)

To braise the tempeh

225 g pack organic tempeh
1 tbsp shoyu
1 tbsp rice mirin
1 tbsp ume plum seasoning
½ tbsp freshly squeezed ginger juice
1 clove garlic, crushed
½ tsp dried mixed herbs

Cut the tempeh into bite-sized cubes. Add all the other ingredients to a jar, close the lid tightly and shake well to mix.

To cook the tempeh

Warm a little filtered water in a heavy-based pan over a low-medium heat, add the tempeh cubes and cook covered for 5 minutes. Pour over the marinade, cover and cook on a low heat for 25 minutes, adding water if the pan dries out. Transfer to a large bowl.

The pastry

Follow the instructions on your pastry packet for thawing. Remove the pastry from the box and lay on a baking tray lined with parchment paper. Let sit for 15 minutes then gently roll and allow the pastry to come to room temperature.

The greens

Bring a small pan of filtered water to a boil. Pop the spinach into a steamer basket. Cover and steam the spinach for a 1–2 minutes until wilted. Transfer to a small plate and set aside.

The mushrooms

In a heavy-based pan, heat a little filtered water and cook the mushrooms with a pinch of sea salt for 7–8 minutes. Add the red wine and allow to soak into the mushrooms;

(continued)

cook until the pan is dry. Remove the mushrooms to a bowl and set aside.

The filling
Using the same pan, add a splash of filtered water and sauté the garlic, leeks, celery, onions and carrots, tamari and herbs. Cook for 5–7 minutes. Remove from the pan and allow the mixture to cool. Add this mixture to the tempeh bowl, use a paper towel to blot any moisture from the mixture, then transfer to a dish and chill in the fridge.

The secret to a deliciously juicy yet flaky wellington is to pat everything dry and make sure it is completely cold before wrapping it in your vegan puff pastry.

Stuffing the wellington
Preheat the oven to 200°C (400°F), gas 6. Layer the mushrooms onto the prepared pastry sheet, spreading them evenly along the edge of the pastry nearest to you. Layer some of the filling on top of the mushrooms, then the spinach, and top with a layer of the steamed carrots. Add a thin layer of basil pesto along the full length of the filling. Very carefully fold the pastry over the top of the mixture and press down to seal the edges. Trim any excess pastry and crimp around the edges with the back of a fork.

Using a sharp knife, score diagonally across the pastry in both directions. Put in a couple of vents by pushing a sharp knife down into the middle of the pastry.

To make the egg wash
    1 tbsp aquafaba (chickpea water)
    1 tbsp almond milk
    ½ tsp maple syrup or brown rice syrup

To make the vegan egg wash, whisk all of the ingredients together in a bowl. Using a pastry brush, very lightly coat the wellington. Place the baking tray with the wellington in the freezer for 10 minutes before repeating with another layer of vegan egg wash, and freezing for a further 10 minutes.

Place the baking tray in the oven for 30–35 minutes, or until golden and flaky. Beautifully layered colours of delicious vegetables encased in puff pastry will be the end result, and served with some shiitake gravy (page 193) is heaven on earth. Makes 8 servings.

Note – Use any remaining filling and leftover pastry to make mini pastries that are great for snacks or picnics. The leftovers also work well as a pie filling.

Roasted Red Pepper and Chickpea Korma

A beautiful, fragrant vegetable chickpea curry with korma spices, made creamy with rich coconut cream and perfectly roasted pumpkin pieces. Served with saffron-scented rice, this is a mellow-spiced and vibrantly coloured dish perfect for the whole family.

1 cup roasted sweet red pepper, cut into small dice
Pinch sea salt
½ tsp cumin seeds
½ tsp turmeric
¼ to ½ tsp mild curry powder
1 red onion, diced
3 cloves garlic, crushed
1 inch (2 cm) piece of fresh ginger, peeled and minced
2 tsp shoyu or tamari
1¼ cups unsweetened coconut cream
4 tbsp nutritional yeast
¼ tsp regular or smoked paprika
1½ cups cooked chickpeas (see page 81)
2 tsp ume paste
Juice of 1 lime
2 tbsp kuzu, dissolved in 2 tbsp filtered water
1 bunch watercress, leaves only, chopped
¼ cup fresh coriander, chopped

In a heavy-based pan, warm a splash or two of filtered water. Add the red pepper, sea salt, cumin seeds, turmeric, and mild curry powder, along with the onion, garlic, ginger and shoyu. Cook over low-medium flame for 5–8 minutes. Transfer the mixture to a high-speed blender along with the coconut cream, nutritional yeast and paprika. Blend to a cream.

Transfer the mixture back to the pan and add the chickpeas and ume paste. Mix well, cover and cook for 15 minutes on a low heat. Add the kuzu and stir continuously until the mixture thickens. Stir in the lime juice and watercress. Garnish with fresh coriander. Makes 4–6 servings. Serve with white fluffy basmati rice and a choice of side dishes if desired.

To cook the rice

2 cups organic basmati rice
3 cups boiling filtered water
¼ tsp sea salt
8–10 saffron threads

Using a strainer, rinse the rice under cold running water. Soak in a large bowl of filtered water for 1 hour. Drain and transfer to a heavy-based pot and add the salt. Pour 3 cups of boiling filtered water over the rice. Spread the saffron threads on top and cook over a medium-high heat. When the water starts boiling and steaming, cover the pot tightly with a heavy lid so that no steam escapes. Turn down the heat to just above its lowest setting, and let the rice cook for 15 minutes undisturbed. I like to use my flame spreader for even heat distribution. Allow the rice to stay covered for another 5 minutes before removing the lid. Transfer to a large bowl. Fluff the rice and serve. Makes 4–6 servings.

(continued)

Top tips for perfect rice – Use the best quality organic basmati rice you can find. Rinsing the rice well helps get rid of starch that can make your rice sticky. Adding salt to the rice in the pot before pouring in the water helps the salt absorb into the grains. Using a tight-fitting cover lets the rice steam perfectly. This method consistently yields long, separate, perfectly steamed fluffy grains of rice.

Note – Roasted chopped sweet red peppers are available in jars – I use them often for quickness. We prefer a mild heat so adjust to your preference. I used ¼ tsp mild curry powder, which is hot enough for us.

Tricolour Quinoa and Vegetable Stir-Fry with Teriyaki Sauce

Use fresh vegetables in season to prepare colourful stir-fries. Try also with pak choi, sweetcorn or garden peas. Add chickpeas or any type of beans – make it your own.

2 cups tricolour quinoa
2⅔ cups filtered water
1 red onion, diced
3 spring onions, diced
Pinch sea salt
1 carrot, cut on the bias
1 cup chestnut mushrooms, sliced
1 yellow pepper, diced
1 courgette, diced
½ head broccoli, cut into small florets

To cook the quinoa

Rinse the quinoa and place in a heavy-based saucepan with the water. Bring to a boil, uncovered. Reduce heat to very low, place a flame spreader under the pot, cover and cook for 10–12 minutes. Remove from the heat and allow to steam for a further 15 minutes with the lid on. Transfer to a large bowl and allow to cool.

Sauce

4 tbsp shoyu or tamari
2 tbsp rice mirin
2 tbsp maple syrup
1 tbsp lime juice and zest of 1 lime
1 tsp garlic, crushed
1 tsp fresh ginger, minced

Garnish

Chopped chives
Toasted flaked almonds

In a small bowl mix the sauce ingredients together and set aside, allowing the flavours to develop. Warm a heavy-based pan, add a splash of filtered water, and sauté the onion and spring onions with a pinch of sea salt. After 5 minutes, add the carrots, mushrooms, pepper, courgette and broccoli. Pour ¼ cup of filtered water over the vegetables, cover the pan and

(continued)

allow the vegetables to cook for 5 minutes. Stir in the teriyaki sauce and sauté for another 5 minutes, mixing well to coat all the vegetables. If the pan seems dry, add a splash of water. Remove from the heat and stir into the cooked quinoa. Serve in warmed bowls and dress with some chopped chives and flaked almonds. Makes 4–6 servings.

Early in our evolution there were three tastes that gave us great pleasure but were very rare: simple sugars, fats and salt. The body's reward system is still labouring under the idea that these tastes are rare and that we may not get more for a long time. They can be triggers to overeating. Sugar is the biggest culprit and one of today's biggest problems. The refined sugars that are so prevalent in the modern diet are the most harmful.

Everyone knows that sugar is a nutritional nightmare. When we eat refined sugar in soft drinks, sweets or other snack foods our blood sugar levels rise quickly, putting stress on the pancreas, liver and other organs to bring it down to a normal range. One of the most serious effects is that it compromises the immune system for several hours. Eating even small amounts of sugar several times a day means that our immunity is shut down most of the time. When we eat a diet with plenty of complex carbohydrate from grains, beans and vegetables, our system uses it slowly, when we need it, and our immunity is supported. Once we have kicked the sugar habit, our taste buds recover and the sugars in fruits and vegetables satisfy our need for the pleasure of sweetness.

Spaghetti with Basil and Watercress Pesto

A quick and easy solution to the shop-bought heavy oil and cheese pesto. This recipe achieves a coarse pesto that blends well with spaghetti or is perfect for spreading on to toasted pitta or sourdough or making bruschetta or pizza. Replace or mix the watercress with a mixture of other organic greens like spinach or rocket.

Pasta

1 pack Italian spaghetti

Cook the spaghetti according to the instructions on the packet. Drain immediately and serve topped with a generous serving of pesto.

Garnish with vegan parmesan (see lasagne recipe, pages 114–116).

Pesto

3 cups tightly packed watercress leaves
2 cups tightly packed fresh basil leaves
½ cup pine nuts
½ cup walnuts
1 ripe avocado, peeled and chopped
2 small cloves garlic, chopped
1 tbsp lemon juice
1 cup filtered water
2 tbsp white miso
3 tbsp nutritional yeast
½ tsp garlic granules
½ tsp onion granules
⅛ tsp sea salt

Put all the ingredients into a food processer. Pulse until you achieve the consistency you desire, adding more water if required. Makes 4–6 servings.

Note – Stores well in the refrigerator up to 1 week, or can be frozen.

Note – Nutritional yeast is the answer to add that cheesy taste to sauces and pastas. This dried yeast is high in B vitamins and umami flavour. The yeast *Saccharomyces cerevisiae*, used for fermenting beer, is made into nutritional yeast by baking at very high temperatures, so the yeast breaks up and gets all crumbly.

 We share the planet with billions of other life forms. There is not one of those creatures that is disposable, and yet humans are directly responsible for the extinction of over 300 species per year. These extinctions were not essential for our survival, but every one of them weakened the web of life that supports all life on the planet. It seems our desire to destroy other creatures has no end. Every year we kill 60 billion land animals and trillions of aquatic creatures for food; 100 million for experimental purposes (often to test cosmetics); 200 million are killed by hunters, and 30 million of those specifically for fur. None of this is required. Veganism means expressing love and respect for all life. A revolution of the heart, as our friend Professor Gary L. Francione said.

Vegan Shepherd's Pie with Shiitake Gravy

In this vegan shepherd's pie, vegetables and lentils mingle in a sumptuous broth beneath a crown of mashed sweet potatoes. This vegan dish takes on the classic family comfort food and will be loved by all. Use white potatoes instead of sweet potatoes if that is your preference.

4 large sweet potatoes, peeled and cubed
1 tbsp paprika
1 tbsp dried parsley
1 large red onion, chopped
2 cloves garlic, crushed
2 cups carrots, diced small
2 cups organic sweetcorn
1 sachet umami instant stock dissolved in
 4 cups boiling filtered water
2 cups red lentils
1 tsp each of thyme, marjoram, basil
2 cups sweet garden peas
1 tsp black pepper (optional)
1 tbsp tamari

Preheat the oven to 180°C (350°F), gas 4. Boil the sweet potatoes until soft, drain, transfer to a large bowl and mash with a fork. Stir in the paprika and parsley and set aside.

In a heavy-based pan, sauté the onion, garlic and carrots, along with the sweetcorn, in a little filtered water until tender, about 7 minutes. Set aside. Place the lentils and umami stock into a pot. Bring to a boil and simmer until soft, about 20 minutes. Add the cooked vegetable mixture, along with the

herbs, sweet garden peas and black pepper, if using. Add the tamari and mix well. If the mixture is too wet, add in some of the sweet potato mash to thicken.

Fill the bottom of a large casserole dish or small individual pie dishes with the lentil and vegetable mixture, and top with the mashed sweet potatoes. Place on a baking tray to catch any overspill. Cook in the middle of the oven for 25–30 minutes. You may also grill for 5 minutes at the end of cooking to crisp up the sweet potato. Serve smothered in shiitake gravy (page 193). Makes 6–8 servings.

 Tradition in many countries dictates a short meditation or prayer before eating. It is important to reflect on how the food found your plate. It needed to be planted, tended, harvested and shipped to you. So many unsung people participated in your good fortune. Such reflection also allows us to slow down and set a new rhythm for our meal, and relax so we can chew our food.

Digestion begins in the mouth. Chewing not only physically breaks down the food, but enzymes in the mouth actually begin to break down carbohydrates. If you chew a mouthful of brown rice, barley or a piece of wholemeal bread for long enough, it will begin to taste sweet. Try this experiment developed in Zen monasteries. After putting food in your mouth, put down your fork, spoon or chopsticks, fold your hands and chew until your food is completely masticated. If you do this for a few times you will realise how little your food is usually chewed.

Fermented beans or vegetables are a hallmark of almost every culture. Fermented soy products in the Far East and fermented grains and vegetables in Western countries were produced in the home or local communities. These foods were a reflection of ancient wisdom regarding the essential nature of a healthy digestive system. Naturally fermented foods provide microorganisms that promote a healthy gut biome. Cooking and fermenting are two ways to create the maximum benefit from a wholefood, plant-based diet. Simply adding a small amount of sauerkraut or naturally fermented pickles to your plate increases the nutritional effectiveness of your food. No need to use expensive probiotic supplements, simply make some pickles at home, as I do, for literally pennies.

In 1962, Rachel Carson wrote a book called *The Silent Spring*. The book called attention to the fact that chemicals being used for pest control were making their way into the food chain. Before the publication of this book there was a passive acceptance that new chemical solutions for the control of insects were a gift from science and harmless to human life. The public acceptance of DDT was based on the naive expectation that any chemical sprays used near human dwellings, school playgrounds or on food plants must have been tested for safety. The battle over pesticides stimulated the organic growing revolution and made the public aware of the dangers of chemical herbicides, pesticides and other toxic chemicals used in farming. The book is still available and just as important now as it was then. Using poison to grow our food is simply another form of suicide.

Where do you get your calcium? Most of us have been taught that the best source of calcium is cows' milk. Very convenient if you are a dairy farmer but, alas, not true. The milk of any mammal is specifically designed to meet the needs of the young of that species. In fact, the best source of calcium is the same one the cow uses: plants. Many commonly used vegetables such as broccoli and kale, beans like black beans and kidney beans, tofu, and grains are all great sources of this vital mineral. The sad irony is that recent scientific studies have shown that women in countries where the most dairy food is used have very high incidence of osteoporosis.

Lip-Smacking Sides and Salads

These delicious side dishes are packed with everything that is good for you and are powerhouses of antioxidants and other nutrients. We eat a fresh salad every single day – either warm or cold, depending on the season. I always buy local and seasonal produce where possible. It's better for the environment and for our health, and they taste so good. I am craving growing my own greens again when we have some outdoor space, but for now my sprouter is always full to the gunnels with sprouted mung beans, lentils and adzuki beans. I add them to all our meals.

- Creamy Coleslaw
- American Noodle Salad
- Couscous Rainbow Salad with Lemon and Lime Tahini Sauce
- Cucumber Wakame and Peach Salad with Ume Tangy Sauce
- Nishime Vegetable Stew
- Nest of Steamed Kale with Pressed Salad and Sweet Vinaigrette
- Asparagus with Vegan Hollandaise Sauce
- Lemon-Scented Arame Sauté with Toasted Walnuts
- Ginger-Glazed Carrots and Watercress
- Roasted Vegetable Combo
- Herb-Crusted Baked Cauliflower
- Crispy Potato Wedges with Ketchup

Creamy Coleslaw

All through the seasons, I have a little raw food on our plates. I created this recipe for Bill as he seriously loves coleslaw. It's a winner with everyone, economical and easy to make. My students love it slathered on toasted sourdough bread.

4 cups white cabbage, finely grated
2 cups carrots, grated
2 cups spring onions, very thinly sliced
1 cup oil-free mayonnaise (page 194)
1 tsp Dijon mustard
¼ cup brown rice vinegar
¼ tsp sea salt

In a small bowl, stir the dressing ingredients together. Allow the mixture to stand for at least 1 hour. Mix the cabbage, carrots and spring onions together in a large salad bowl. Add the dressing to the vegetables and stir well. Allow to chill for 1 hour or more before serving. Keep refrigerated for up to 7 days in a sealed container. Makes 6–8 servings.

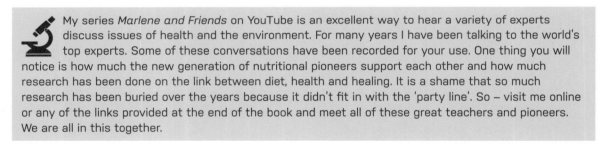 My series *Marlene and Friends* on YouTube is an excellent way to hear a variety of experts discuss issues of health and the environment. For many years I have been talking to the world's top experts. Some of these conversations have been recorded for your use. One thing you will notice is how much the new generation of nutritional pioneers support each other and how much research has been done on the link between diet, health and healing. It is a shame that so much research has been buried over the years because it didn't fit in with the 'party line'. So – visit me online or any of the links provided at the end of the book and meet all of these great teachers and pioneers. We are all in this together.

American Noodle Salad

Here is the basic formula for creating an endless variety of wholesome, tasty, and brilliantly colourful pasta salads based on what you find throughout the seasons. Always a great hit among the 'mixed' crowd of vegans and non-vegans.

1 pack corn and rice fusilli pasta

For the dressing
1 cup oil-free mayonnaise (page 194)
1½ tbsp brown rice vinegar
2 tsp Dijon mustard
2 tsp brown rice syrup
2 tbsp juice from dill pickles or ume plum vinegar

For the salad
1 cup roasted red pepper, cut into small dice
1 cup carrots, grated
1 cup olives, black and green, chopped
1 cup celery, cut into small dice
1 cup cucumber, peeled and cut into small dice
2 cups spring onions, sliced thinly on the diagonal
1 cup red radishes, very thinly sliced
1 cup dill pickles, cut into small dice
½ cup fresh parsley, minced
½ cup fresh coriander, minced

Garnish
Red and green chicory leaves
Chopped chives and roasted pine nuts

In a medium bowl, mix together the ingredients for the dressing and set aside. Cook the pasta according to the packet instructions. Remove from the heat and rinse in cold water until completely cooled. Transfer the pasta to a large bowl. Add all the vegetables herbs and mix well. Stir in the dressing and garnish with the chives and roasted pine nuts. Decorate with the green and red chicory leaves. Enjoy my bowl of sunshine. Makes 6–8 servings.

Couscous Rainbow Salad with Lemon and Lime Tahini Sauce

This easy salad is inspired by rich Middle Eastern flavours. Served with couscous and drizzled with a sweet, sharp dressing and toasted pine nuts, it is filling and delicious. Vibrant colours are matched with clear flavours in a beautiful, interesting salad dish.

3 cups cooked couscous
1 small cucumber, cut into ribbons
1 cup carrots, shredded
3 spring onions, sliced
1 cup orange pieces
1 cup peach slices
½ cup red radishes, thinly sliced
¼ cup currants or dried cranberries
½ cup fresh parsley, chopped
¼ cup fresh mint, chopped
½ cup toasted flaked almonds
1 cup steamed broccoli florets

For the couscous

3 cups couscous
4½ cups boiling filtered water
Pinch sea salt
1 tsp dried mixed herbs

Dressing

Lemon and lime tahini sauce (pages 191–192)

Garnish

¼ cup toasted pine nuts

Spread the couscous evenly in the bottom of a large casserole so that it is in as thin a layer as possible. Add the salt and herbs to boiling filtered water and gently pour over the couscous. Cover tightly with a lid or compostable cling film. Set aside for about 15 minutes, then fluff with a fork.

Cut the cucumber lengthwise into ⅛-inch-thick ribbons using a mandolin or other manual slicer.

In a large bowl, combine the cooked couscous with the remaining ingredients. Pour over the sauce and mix well. Garnish with toasted pine nuts. Makes 6–8 servings.

Note – Try experimenting with different seasonal vegetables as you make this salad throughout the year. Carrots, celery, mushrooms, spring onions, leeks, artichokes, raisins or chopped apricots all work well in this versatile dish.

Cucumber Wakame and Peach Salad with Ume Tangy Sauce

This cucumber wakame salad is light and refreshing and a great start to any meal. I enjoy this fresh salad as a starter to a sushi dinner, or on its own for a light lunch. Wakame is a seaweed rich in vitamins and minerals that helps to balance hormones, among many health benefits. Wakame is paired with my choice of vegetables and fruits in this recipe to make a simple side salad. Cos or romaine (Romano) lettuce is long and almost oblong in shape. The leaves are thick and firm with a stiff central rib. The outer leaves are slightly bitter, but the ones in the centre are sweeter and more delicate.

¼ cup wakame flakes
1 head romaine (Romano) lettuce
1 pack mixed salad greens
1 cup sugar snap peas, blanched and left whole
1 small carrot, peeled and cut into flowers
1 small cucumber, peeled and cut into flowers
1 cup peach slices
2 tbsp white sesame seeds

Tangy umeboshi dressing
1 tbsp umeboshi paste
4 tbsp rice mirin
2 tbsp tamari
2 tbsp brown rice syrup

To make the cucumber and carrot flowers
Use a tool called a channel knife (available from kitchen shops). Lay the carrot and cucumber on a flat chopping board. Starting at the top, dig the knife into the vegetable and draw the channel down to the end. Turn the vegetable over and do the same on the other side. Repeat until you have created four equal channels. This will then create the flowers in my photograph.

Mix all the ingredients for the umeboshi dressing in a large bowl. Set aside to allow the flavours to develop. Soak the wakame in cold filtered water for 20 minutes, drain and set aside. Blanch the sugar snap peas in boiling filtered water for 1 minute then rinse under cold running water. Cut the romaine lettuce into wedges.

Toss the wakame, salad greens, sugar snap peas, and carrot and cucumber flowers together in a large bowl. Pour over the dressing and mix well, coating all the vegetables. Add the peach slices and sesame seeds and gently toss to mix. Makes 6–8 servings.

 In the summer, when the sun is at its height, the fruits and softer vegetables ripen. The summer vegetables have a higher concentration of fluid. Fruits and salad vegetables proliferate, and help cool the body down and refresh the senses. Salads and light cooking are the order of the day. This season is associated with the functions of the heart in Chinese medicine. Bitter-tasting foods such as bitter greens, chicory, kale and collard greens can be incorporated in salads, and provide a valuable tonic for the heart.

Nishime Vegetable Stew

Nishime, or water braising of vegetables, calls for large pieces or chunks of root vegetables cooked over a low heat until they are tender and sweet. The steam generated by this method of cooking allows the vegetables to cook in their own juices, eliminating the need for anything more than just a little added water. A light seasoning towards the end of cooking brings out their full-bodied flavour and natural sweetness.

Vegetables cooked in this manner are quite soft and juicy, giving us a very warming, strengthening energy. This is one of my favourite macrobiotic dishes, which I use with all my clients. This dish has the ability to strengthen the body's core organs, such as the pancreas and spleen. This enhances the whole digestive system. A great dish for creating vitality and one to be incorporated into your diet over the long term.

A small piece of kombu in the bottom of the pot brings out the sweetness of the vegetables, naturally tenderises them by virtue of its glutamic acid and lightly mineralises the dish, helping to create strong blood.

3 inch (7 cm) piece of kombu seaweed
1 dried shiitake mushroom
¼ cup filtered water
1 small cabbage
1 small butternut squash
1 large carrot
1 red onion
1 white onion
Shoyu

Soak the kombu and shiitake in the water for 15 minutes, then place in a heavy pot. Peel and chop the vegetables into bite-sized pieces and arrange the vegetables in the pot in individual sections. Check there is enough water to just cover the bottom of the pot. Bring to a boil over a medium heat, reduce the heat to low, cover and cook until the vegetables are tender, about 25–40 minutes. Season the vegetables lightly with shoyu and simmer 10 minutes more, until all the liquid has been absorbed by the vegetables. If the water evaporates too quickly during cooking, add a little more and reduce the heat (because it is cooking too quickly). Transfer to a bowl and serve. For variety, use Brussels sprouts, leeks, parsnips, turnips, green cabbage or whatever vegetables are seasonally available. Makes 4–6 servings.

The Japanese have a saying, 'soil and man, not two'. It is an acknowledgement that all plant life is dependent on a living soil. Dead soil means a dead planet. The terrestrial food chain begins with the soil. Many people who advocate organic, chemical-free farming methods stress the danger of unwanted toxins in the food. Of course, this is important, but intensive chemical use is a greater hazard, in its effect on the life of the soil. More creatures live within the soil than in any other environment on the planet. It is the single most diverse ecosystem. Any way of eating that undermines healthy, living soil is by definition poor nutrition. A single teaspoon (1 gram) of rich garden soil can hold up to one billion bacteria, several yards of fungal filaments, several thousand protozoa and scores of nematodes. These tiny life forms are the foundation of all life on the planet.

Nest of Steamed Kale with Pressed Salad and Sweet Vinaigrette

Kale is one of the kings of our greens. Teamed with pickles or ginger, it's a daily staple for us. It is worth the investment to buy a good pickle press to make quick pickles and pressed salads. Any pickled or pressed salads create a healthy intestinal tract by increasing the digestive enzymes to allow better absorption of nutrients from your food.

> 1 large bunch of kale

Wash the kale and remove the leaves, discarding the fibrous stem or saving it for making vegetable stock. Tear the leaves into pieces and place in a steamer basket. Bring a small amount of filtered water to a boil in a pot, and once boiling pop on the steamer basket and steam the kale for 4–5 minutes until vibrant green.

Pressed salad with sweet vinaigrette

> 1 cucumber, sliced into thin rounds
> 2 cups red radish, sliced into thin rounds
> ⅛ tsp sea salt
> 1 tbsp toasted white sesame seeds

Sweet vinaigrette

> ¼ cup brown rice vinegar
> ¼ cup mirin
> Pinch sea salt

Place the vegetables and sea salt in a small bowl and mix. If you don't have a pickle press, keep the vegetables in the bowl and put a weight on a plate directly on top of the vegetables. Allow to sit for at least 1 hour. Warm the rice vinegar and mirin with the salt in a small saucepan. Set aside and allow to cool. Squeeze any excess liquid from the salad by gently squeezing the vegetables. Toss with the dressing and sprinkle with toasted white sesame seeds. Makes 4–6 servings.

 Autumn can be a difficult season for our health. Many people indulge themselves in the summer months and run down their immunity. In Chinese medicine autumn is referred to as representing metal energy. This has to do with the firming up of the body and the retention of minerals. It is interesting that they predicted that this season was particularly important for the lungs. What we know now is that autumn is challenging to the respiratory system. This presents itself in increased colds, flu and complaints such as asthma. Outdoor allergies may flare up at this time of year. The counterbalance for these is to eat only warming foods, lots of dark green vegetables (particularly cruciferous vegetables such as broccoli, cabbage and kale). Seasoning foods with a pungent taste such as ginger, garlic, onion or a little pepper helps to stimulate the lungs.

Asparagus with Vegan Hollandaise Sauce

Asparagus is one of the first crops of spring. Paired with rich-tasting vegan 'hollandaise' sauce, it makes the perfect vegetable side dish for any special meal. I also serve asparagus spears in salads, and often roast it with garlic in the oven. A versatile and nutrient-dense vegetable.

    1 large bunch asparagus, trimmed
    1 tbsp fresh lemon juice
    1 tsp tamari or shoyu
    2 tbsp nutritional yeast
    1 tsp Dijon mustard
    ½ tsp tahini
    ½ cup soft silken tofu, drained
    ¼ tsp turmeric

Garnish
    Sprinkling of turmeric

Bring a small pot of filtered water to a boil. Pop the asparagus into a steamer basket. Cover, and steam the asparagus for 4–6 minutes or just until crisp and tender. Meanwhile, blend all the other ingredients to a smooth cream in a high-speed blender. Transfer to a small saucepan and cook over a low heat, stirring constantly, until heated through. Arrange the hot asparagus on a serving platter and pour the sauce over top. Serve immediately and dust lightly with turmeric. Makes 4–6 servings.

Lemon-Scented Arame Sauté with Toasted Walnuts

With its sweet, mild flavour, arame is an excellent choice for introducing sea vegetables into your daily diet. Its rich black colour adds vivid contrast and beauty to any meal. Arame contributes an exotic flair to salads, and is delicious when sautéed with carrots and onions or with dried tofu. I always introduce my clients and students who have never tried seaweed before to this sea vegetable, and it's a winner with everyone.

1 cup arame seaweed
2 onions, finely sliced
Pinch sea salt
1 tbsp shoyu
1 tbsp apple juice concentrate
Lemon rind, finely grated
Toasted walnuts for garnish

Rinse and soak the arame seaweed in cold filtered water for 20 minutes. Sauté the onions in a little filtered water with a pinch of sea salt for 5 minutes uncovered, until they are translucent. Drain the arame and add to the onions, together with just enough water to cover them. Cover and simmer gently until the water has been absorbed, approximately 20 minutes. Season to taste with some shoyu, apple juice concentrate and lemon rind. Garnish with toasted walnuts. Makes 4–6 servings.

Ginger-Glazed Carrots and Watercress

Watercress is a free-floating hollow-stemmed plant. Its small, oval, dark green, succulent leaves carry a high moisture content. The greens feature a sharp, peppery and slightly tangy taste, somewhat like that of tender mustard greens and garden cress. It is an often-overlooked leafy green food source that is a close cousin to mustard greens, cabbage and arugula. I adore it and use it in soups, stews and salads. In fact, I have even been known to eat a bunch while de-stemming it. One of my favourite greens for sure. Make sure you remove the thickest stems if you're eating it raw.

3 carrots, thinly julienned
1 cup cold filtered water
2 cups watercress, chopped
1 tsp shoyu
1 heaped tsp kuzu
2 tsp juice squeezed from freshly grated ginger
Pinch of sea salt

Heat a splash of filtered water in a pan, add the carrots and mix with a wooden spoon. Sauté for about 5 minutes. Add the 1 cup of water and the salt, cover and simmer over a low heat for 10 minutes, until the carrots are just tender. Add the greens and shoyu, mix together and simmer for 5 minutes. Take the pan off the heat. Dissolve the kuzu in a tablespoon of cold filtered water and slowly add it to the vegetables. Put the pan back on the heat and bring to a simmer, while you continue to stir. Cook for another couple of minutes and then add the ginger juice. Mix and serve as a side dish. Makes 4–6 servings.

Roasted Vegetable Combo

What vegetables to roast? Root vegetables like potatoes, parsnips, sweet potatoes and carrots are old standbys when it comes to roasting, of course, but there are all sorts of wonderful concoctions you can come up with. From cruciferous vegetables like broccoli and Brussels sprouts to courgettes, onions and bell peppers. I often make a batch of oven-roasted root vegetables and store leftovers for the next day's lunch.

2 parsnips, peeled and thickly sliced
2 large red beetroots, scrubbed, peeled and quartered
2 large carrots, cut into thick spears
1 large sweet potato, cut into thick spears
2 large red onions, peeled and thickly sliced
1 courgette, cut into irregular chunks
6 cloves of garlic, in skins (remove after roasting)
2 tbsp balsamic vinegar
Sea salt and freshly ground pepper
1 tbsp mixed herbs

Preheat the oven to 190°C (375°F), gas 5. In a large bowl, toss the vegetables in the balsamic vinegar. Add some sea salt and freshly ground black pepper. Sprinkle with a spoonful of your favourite herbs: oregano, thyme, rosemary, sage, parsley or basil, and mix well. Transfer the vegetables to a parchment-lined roasting tin. Roast the vegetables for about 1 hour, stirring them at least twice through the cooking time. If you prefer your vegetables less cooked, shorten the roasting time. The balsamic vinegar and sea salt make for fabulous roasting, complementing the caramelised sweetness with a perfect touch of salty-tart. Makes 4–6 servings.

Note – Cut the vegetables correctly. A good rule of thumb is the denser the vegetables the smaller the cut, so cut root vegetables like sweet potatoes, carrots, parsnip and turnip smaller than the more open vegetables like broccoli and cauliflower. This ensures that the vegetables cook evenly and will be done at the same time.

Herb-Crusted Baked Cauliflower

Cauliflower is incredibly versatile as you will see from the wealth of recipes available, ranging from curries to soups to the comforting creamy cauliflower mash. It's inexpensive and local and ticks all the right boxes. Roasted whole, it makes a wonderful addition to a family feast. Adapt this recipe with other herbs and spices to the way it works for you.

1 cup ground almonds
¼ cup nutritional yeast
½ tsp garlic granules
½ tsp Italian seasoning
¼ tsp sea salt
⅔ cup filtered water
1 tsp Dijon mustard
1 head cauliflower, cut into florets
Fresh herbs to serve

Preheat the oven to 180°C (350°F), gas 4. Combine the almonds, nutritional yeast and seasonings in a bowl. Using a whisk, add water gradually. Stir in the mustard. The mixture should resemble a thick batter.

Toss the cauliflower florets in the coating. Place on a parchment-lined baking sheet and bake for 20–25 minutes, until the coating is dry and crisp and the cauliflower is tender. Makes 4–6 servings.

Crispy Potato Wedges with Ketchup

Who doesn't love potato wedges with a dip? Sweet or spicy, these potato wedges are crispy and crackly on the outside, with tender potato inside. They're the perfect homemade solution. Coat generously with your choice of seasonings. Choose a potato like the ones I've listed below for their fluffy texture, which means they're best suited to roasting, baking or chipping.

    4 medium-large King Edward or Yukon potatoes
    1 tbsp plain flour
    ½ tsp sea salt
    1 tsp paprika
    1 tsp garlic granules
    1 tsp onion granules
    ⅛ tsp black pepper

In a small bowl, combine the flour and seasonings, mix well and set aside. Wash the potatoes, half and quarter them into equal-sized wedges. Place the potatoes in a heavy-based pot with a pinch or two of sea salt, and cover with filtered water. Bring to a boil, then cover with a lid, reduce heat to medium and cook for 15 minutes. Drain transfer a large bowl. Leave for 5 minutes to allow the steam to evaporate.

Preheat the oven to 200°C (400°F), gas 6. Line a roasting tin with parchment paper. Sprinkle the seasoning over the wedges, taking care when mixing not to break the potatoes. Spread potatoes out evenly in the roasting tin and bake for 30–35 minutes, or until crisp and golden around the edges. Remove from the oven and serve with some ketchup (page 185). Makes 4 servings. Double or triple the quantities as and when required.

To get the same number of calories in our food you have to use 100 times the amount of **water** when using animals as compared to plants. Our 'water footprint' is equally important to our 'carbon footprint'. It takes about 15,000 litres of water to produce a kilogram of beef. When you see a piece of meat in the supermarket, try to imagine how many bottles of water went into the piece of flesh. When we compare this to eating a plant-based diet, we see the remarkable difference. A kilogram of rice takes only 2,400 litres of water and a kilogram of potatoes takes 287 litres. By shifting our food from animal-sourced to our Human Ecology Diet we not only lower our water footprint, we also contribute to cleaner water.

Geneticists have known for several decades that most of the genome (the DNA) – 98% – does not consist of 'normal' genes that code for proteins. This non-coding DNA was originally thought of as 'junk DNA' – having no function – but a lot of it has since been discovered to regulate the expression of genes. Part of the non-coding DNA consists of 'pseudogenes', which are imperfect copies of functional genes. These genes have been referred to as 'genetic fossils' (they used to be functional, but have accumulated mutations over time that stop them from 'working'), and so may often represent functions that have been lost. Some have been found to still have a regulatory effect, sometimes on their 'parent' gene (the one of which they are an imperfect copy).

One of the most interesting examples of a high concentration of pseudogenes is in the genes for sense perception, particularly for smell and taste. One theory is that our primitive ancestors needed a broader range of smell and taste receptors to detect food that was potentially harmful. Our hunter-gatherer ancestors would most likely been excellent detectors of any toxic factors in their food. The good news is that some of this capacity still exists, but we have to exercise the function to regain it. If you eat simple nutritious food (such as the Human Ecology Diet), you will find many common processed foods begin to taste vile. Your body knows it simply needs a rest from the fat, animal protein and chemical deluge that have dulled the senses.

We always find it interesting how many people assume that any problem they have is 'genetic'. I guess it is easy to blame the family or put the causes of our problems outside our control. It is interesting to note here that it is usually the first thing your doctor will tell you. You have a certain disease because of your genes. This is especially true with cancer and other serious health issues.

Breast cancer is common, but most women with the disease do not have a strong family history of it. Less than one in ten have a genetic link. This is all down to the difference between having a particular gene and the expression of that gene. From my studies with T. Colin Campbell I learned that although all diseases have some genetic basis, direct or indirect, **it is the control of gene 'expression' by nutrition that matters far more than the mere presence or absence of mutated genes**. 'Infectious diseases have a microbial basis but our susceptibility to these diseases depends on our immune system whose response has a genetic basis.'* Your stress levels, social surroundings, physical activity and overall lifestyle all contribute to your gene expression – or how your cells respond. Diet is key in this process. The nutrients in your food interact with your genes. We do not control everything, but we can control our diet. Diet is the simplest and most effective way to prevent disease. The Human Ecology Diet conforms to what leading-edge nutrition has to offer for a healthy life. I share my mantra with literally everyone who breathes:

*Food makes the blood, blood makes the cells,
cells make the tissue, tissue makes the organs and here we be.*

It's that simple.

---

*From 'Musings about Science', by T. Colin Campbell PhD, August 2014, nutritionstudies.org.

Delish and Divine Sauces, Dressings and Dips

- Ketchup
- Sour Cream
- Classic Hummus
- Salsa
- Guacamole
- Thai Dressing
- Basil and Watercress Pesto
- Lemon and Lime Tahini Sauce
- Marlene's Rich Tomato Sauce
- Rich Shiitake Gravy
- Oil-Free Mayonnaise

Ketchup

Sour cream

Classic hummus

Salsa

Guacamole

Thai dressing

Ketchup

Ketchup is a condiment consisting of puréed tomatoes, onions, vinegar, sweetener, spices, etc., that can be easily made at home. A lot of shop-bought ketchups have many added ingredients that are unnecessary. This ketchup recipe works well in terms of taste, texture and colour.

    1 cup tomato passata
    2 tbsp apple cider vinegar
    2 tbsp maple syrup
    ½ tsp sea salt
    1 tsp garlic granules
    1 tsp onion powder
    ½ tsp oregano
    ¼ tsp ground cinnamon
    1 tbsp kuzu
    2 tbsp filtered water

Blend all the ingredients except the kuzu and water in a high-speed blender on high for 30 to 60 seconds, until well combined and smooth. Transfer the mixture to a medium saucepan over a high heat and bring to a simmer. Continue to simmer, stirring occasionally, for about 30 minutes, until the mixture has reduced and thickened. In a small bowl, combine the kuzu and filtered water. Stir the paste into the tomato mixture, and simmer for 5 minutes more, until thickened further. Remove the pan from the heat, and let the ketchup cool to room temperature. The mixture will continue to thicken as it cools. Transfer to a glass container, seal tightly, and chill in the fridge. Makes 4–6 servings.

Sour Cream

This vegan sour cream takes less than 5 minutes to make, and you can adjust the lemon juice, vinegar, and mustard to taste. This is a great staple to add to your repertoire and will keep in the fridge for about 5 days. Use this healthy dairy alternative in any dish that calls for sour cream. Serve it with baked potatoes and fresh chives, with tacos or enchiladas, or with bean soups – the possibilities are endless.

    300 g pack organic silken tofu
    2 tbsp fresh lemon juice
    1 tbsp ume plum vinegar
    1 tsp Dijon mustard

¼ tsp sea salt
½ tsp onion powder
½ tsp garlic powder
1 tbsp finely chopped chives to serve

Drain the liquid from the tofu. Place all of the ingredients except the chives into a blender. Blend on high for 30 to 60 seconds until smooth and creamy. Stir the chives through (if desired) and serve. Makes 1½ cups.

There is much confusion regarding the use of soy products. One popular myth is that all soy is genetically modified (GM). Let's deal with the facts. Most soybeans are GM, but 85% are fed to farmed animals and the rest are used in commercial food products. Those products that use non-GM are clearly labelled. Most non-GM soy is used in making products such as tofu, soya milk, tempeh, miso and natural soy sauce. The second great myth has to do with a connection between soy consumption and cancer. This myth probably began as a misunderstanding of the fact that soy contains phytoestrogens – not oestrogen. Phytoestrogens mimic the naturally occurring hormone but are not the same. The truth is that people who regularly use tofu, miso and other soy products have been shown to have reduced rates of cancer. The greatest human exposure to oestrogen is through eating farm-raised animals – the hormone is used to promote growth in cows, pigs and chickens. The only caution that we have is using soy milk, particularly for infants, because unfermented soy products can be difficult to digest.

Classic Hummus

Hummus is an absolute staple in our home cuisine. Rarely a week goes by without a dish of hummus at the table. This simple food is tasty, filling and seriously heart healthy. This classic hummus recipe is quick and easy to make, smooth and creamy, perfect for dipping or spreading, and it tastes so fresh and flavourful!

2 garlic cloves, minced
2 cups cooked chickpeas
Grated zest of 1 lemon
1 tbsp lemon juice
⅓ cup sesame tahini
1 tsp ume paste
1 tbsp sweet white miso
1 tsp cumin (optional)
4 fresh basil leaves
2 tbsp filtered water

To cook the chickpeas

1 cup dried chickpeas

Rinse the chickpeas, place into a large bowl and cover with filtered water. Let them soak overnight. Drain and rinse and transfer to a pressure cooker. Use enough water to cover, about 1 inch (2 cm) above the chickpeas. Bring to full pressure then reduce to medium and cook for 50 minutes. Turn off the heat and allow the pressure to release naturally.

Combine all the ingredients in a food processor. Purée until smooth, adding more water if the mixture seems too thick for your taste. Makes 4–6 servings.

My two-minute lunch: Making hummus wraps

Corn or wholewheat soft tortillas
Hummus
Romaine lettuce leaves
Alfalfa sprouts
Sliced tomatoes

To assemble the wraps, lay a soft tortilla on a dry work surface, add the lettuce, sprouts and tomato slices. Spoon the hummus generously over the top, roll, Swiss-roll style, slice in half crosswise and enjoy. Works well with pitta too, and is delicious when warmed first.

Salsa

Salsa is any one of several sauces typical of Mexican cuisine, also known as salsa fresca, hot salsa or salsa picante, particularly when used as a dip. Try this tasty tomato salsa, full of rich flavours. Works great with Mexican tortilla chips or as a topping for enchiladas and burritos.

12 plum tomatoes
6 large shallots, peeled
6 cloves fresh garlic, peeled, left whole
Sea salt
2 chillies (optional) if you like a hot taste
1 tbsp grated lime zest
1 tbsp freshly squeezed lime juice
1 tsp dried rosemary
1 tsp brown rice syrup

Preheat the oven to 160°C (325°F), gas 3. Quarter the tomatoes, leaving the skin and seeds intact. Arrange the tomato pieces on a parchment-lined baking sheet, open side down. Place the shallots and garlic over the top of the tomatoes. Sprinkle with sea salt. Roast for around 45 minutes to 1 hour, until the vegetables are beginning to dry. Allow the tomatoes to cool, and peel. Using a sharp knife, mince all the vegetables and transfer to a mixing bowl. Stir in the lime zest and juice, rosemary, and rice syrup. Adjust seasonings to taste. Mix well and allow to stand for about an hour before serving. Makes 4–6 servings.

Note – Soak chillies (if using) in very hot filtered water for 10 minutes, drain and remove the stems. Split lengthwise, remove seeds and finely mince. Add to the salsa and mix well.

Guacamole

This quick and easy recipe makes a delicious spread for toast and crackers, or a dip for sticks of celery and cucumber. Use soft, ripe avocados; the skin should peel easily, and the flesh should be easy to mash.

    1 large or 2 small ripe avocados, peeled and pitted
    ¼ small red onion, minced
    1 tsp umeboshi paste
    1 tsp lemon juice

Mash the avocados with a fork. Add all the other ingredients and mix well. Serve with hot pitta bread and olives. Works well as a side dish for my enchiladas, with a big bowl of corn chips. Makes 4–6 servings.

The expression of our genes shifts quite dramatically with the changes in season. These changes can affect up to 25% of the genetic code that influences our physical behaviour. The focus of these changes is the expression of genes that affect the immune system and the inflammatory response. These changes show the degree to which our body is still attempting to create a balance with natural process. The changes in gene expression vary with the season so that we are better prepared to adapt to changes in temperature or other seasonal challenges. This is where we might find a useful insight into food selection. Seasonal eating is often perceived as a way to cut down on wasteful food transport and support local agriculture; it is a wise solution to a very real problem. It also seems it could have a direct effect on our health. If the body adapts to the season, then the foods traditionally eaten at that time of year may well be of assistance in creating harmony with that change.

Thai Dressing

I made this dressing for a TV show I presented, and it was a winner with the crew. It is just perfect over grains, salads or vegetables, and works well in tempeh or tofu dishes.

½ cup organic tahini
⅛ cup freshly grated ginger juice
⅛ cup brown rice syrup
3 tbsp lemon juice
3 tbsp tamari
1 large clove garlic
½ cup shredded coconut
1 cup filtered water (to start with)

Blend all the ingredients together in a high-speed blender. Add filtered water as necessary for your desired consistency. Store in a sealed glass jar in the refrigerator. The dressing will thicken as it stands so thin as necessary each time when using. Makes 4–6 servings.

We know that fats are an essential part of human nutrition, so the issue is where these fats come from and how they are used in the body. The majority of fats in the modern diet come from animals. These are in the form of fats in meats or the fats in milk, cheese, butter and other rendered products. Fats are solid at room temperature. Oils are like fats but are liquid at room temperature, and they are usually derived from seeds or nuts. Over the past several decades, the nutritional implications of dietary fats and oils have been studied in depth. The results are interesting. Aside from the 'mouth feel' that fats impart on food and the lubrication in frying, there is no nutritional reason to add fats to our food. In fact, they appear to be harmful. The case against animal fats is the artery-clogging cholesterols found in them (for more information, see the 'Human Ecology Diet' chapter). Vegetable oils create problems as well. The truth is that all vegetable oils can cause the blood to 'sludge'. This is a condition that inhibits circulation by coating cells with excess fats. Nuts and seeds can provide all the fats we need for a healthy life and for improved circulation. I use no oil and yet the taste and textures of the food are delicious.

Lemon and lime tahini sauce

Basil and watercress pesto

Rich shiitake gravy

Marlene's rich tomato sauce

Oil-free mayonnaise

Basil and Watercress Pesto

You can whizz up your own delicious pesto in under 15 minutes – it's great for a fast-fix meal. Walnuts and watercress are a fabulous combination for any of your pesto dishes. Another variation I often use to make pesto is rocket and sunflower seeds. All of these ingredients will provide a freshness to your dish.

3 cups tightly packed watercress leaves
2 cups tightly packed fresh basil leaves
½ cup pine nuts
½ cup walnuts
1 ripe avocado
2 cloves garlic, chopped
1 tbsp lemon juice
1 cup filtered water
2 tbsp white miso
3 tbsp nutritional yeast
½ tsp garlic granules
½ tsp onion granules
⅛ tsp sea salt

Put all of the ingredients into a food processer. Pulse until you achieve the consistency you desire, adding more water if required. Makes 4–6 servings.

 The main cause of the pollution of ground water, aquifers, lakes, reservoirs and rivers is agriculture. The damage that is done by conventional agriculture kills the soil and infects the oceans as well. The runoff of chemical fertilisers and other agricultural toxins pollutes waterways and kills life in lakes and rivers. When this toxic broth makes its way into rivers and the sea, it kills the aquatic life, creating 'dead zones'. There are now over 400 of these dead zones in the oceans of the world, where nothing except algae survive. Waste and ammonia turn into nitrates that reduce the oxygen and kill many aquatic animals. Just one of many reasons to support local organic farms and food producers.

Lemon and Lime Tahini Sauce

2 tbsp sweet white miso
2 tbsp organic white tahini
1 tsp lemon juice
Zest of 1 small lime
1 tsp brown rice syrup
1 tsp ume plum seasoning

½ tsp oregano
Pinch celery seeds
Splash of tamari
Filtered water

Mix all of the ingredients together in a small bowl, adding water gradually until thick and creamy. Makes 4–6 servings.

 Your gut is a very delicate ecosystem, with a greater number of healthy bacterial cells in your gut flora than the number of cells in your body. When this ecosystem is healthy, your digestive tract has the proper balance of stomach acids and bacteria. Disturbances in the gut flora can result in headaches, mood issues, weight gain, menstrual cramps, fatigue, back pain, frequent colds, oestrogen dominance, and more. If your digestive health is poor, everything suffers. The lining in your gut is actually part of your immune system. In fact, it's your first line of defence against harmful organisms that can make you ill.

In addition to the central nervous system of the brain and spinal cord, there is a nervous system in the gut called the enteric nervous system, which sends signals to the brain and vice versa. If you are anxious, depressed or stressed, you may notice that your desire for food is different or your digestion is off. Stress hormones can shut down digestion. The phrases 'rely on your gut' and 'gut instinct' make sense when you realise you have a second 'brain' in your gut.

Marlene's Rich Tomato Sauce

This basic tomato sauce goes with just about everything. It's fantastic for pizza bases and adding to pasta, and is a delicious sauce for lasagne. I make batches and freeze in portion sizes.

Note – For quickness, you can purchase an organic tomato-based sauce.

3 cloves garlic, minced
1 onion, diced
Pinch sea salt
12 large organic tomatoes, diced
1 carrot, diced
1 tsp dried basil
1 tsp dried oregano
2 tbsp nutritional yeast
2 bay leaves
4 sprigs fresh basil, leaves removed and minced

In a heavy-based pan, warm a splash or two of filtered water and sauté the garlic and onion for 5 minutes, adding a pinch of salt to help bring out the sweetness of the onions. Add the tomatoes, carrot, basil, oregano, nutritional yeast and bay leaves. Bring to a boil, reduce heat to low and simmer, covered, for 40 minutes. Remove the bay leaves, stir in the fresh basil and cook uncovered for a further 10 minutes. Using a stick blender, blend for a few minutes in the pan, leaving the sauce quite 'chunky'. You can also stir in the fresh basil after the blending stage. Makes 4 cups.

Rich Shiitake Gravy

Bring on the gravy! This shiitake mushroom gravy is full of flavour and is perfect for anytime of the year. Serve this luscious, low-fat mushroom gravy over mashed potatoes, wellington or shepherd's pie. It's easy to make, comforting and delicious!

    4 inch (10 cm) piece of kombu
    3 dried shiitake mushrooms
    2 cups fresh shiitake mushrooms, thinly sliced
    1 small onion, diced
    2 cloves garlic, chopped
    1 heaped tbsp kuzu
    1 tbsp tamari or shoyu
    2 tbsp rice mirin
    ½ teaspoon dried thyme

Soak the kombu and dried shiitake mushrooms in 3 cups of filtered water for 30 minutes. Remove the mushrooms from the water and slice the caps thinly, discarding the stems. Reserve the soaking water. Heat a splash or two of filtered water in a saucepan and sauté the dried shiitakes, fresh mushrooms, garlic and onion over a medium heat for about 5 minutes. Dissolve the kuzu in two tablespoons of filtered water. Add to the saucepan and stir constantly while slowly adding the soaking water. Keep stirring until the gravy begins to simmer and thicken. Add the tamari or shoyu, mirin, and thyme and simmer gently for 15 minutes. Thin to your desired consistency. Makes 4–6 servings.

Modern science has given us many important insights into human disease processes. This does not mean that indigenous cultures and ancient societies have nothing to offer. Primitive people understood the intimate relationship between human life and the environment. Over the centuries they gained valuable insights into the nutritive and healing properties of plants such as dried shiitake and maitake mushrooms. There are many modern drugs that are based on traditional herbal medicine. Treatments for malaria, cognitive dysfunctions and many common aliments came to us via the traditional medicines of India, China and a variety of other cultures from around the world. A good example of this is ephedrine, used for the treatment of asthma and known to the Chinese for thousands of years.

Oil-Free Mayonnaise

This light mayonnaise is creamy and rich, with a tangy, sweet flavour, and no oil. The cashews give it an incredibly silky texture. Try this delicious mayonnaise on sandwiches, potato salad and more!

¾ cup cashew nuts, soaked overnight
1 cup soy milk
2 tbsp apple cider vinegar
1 tsp Dijon mustard
1 tsp lemon juice
¼ tsp sea salt
4 tsp agar flakes
3 tbsp kuzu or cornflour
¾ cup cold filtered water

Drain and rinse the cashews. Put into a blender with the soy milk, vinegar, mustard, lemon juice, salt and agar flakes. Puree to a cream. Dissolve the kuzu or cornflour in the water. Place in a small saucepan and bring to a boil over a very low heat, stirring constantly. When the mixture becomes translucent, thick and smooth, remove from the heat. Add this mixture to the blender and blend once more, until smooth. Pour into storage jars and refrigerate at least 4 hours. The mayonnaise will continue to thicken when chilling. Makes 2 cups.

Sweet Nosh

Who says you can't have your cake and eat it? Not me. Welcome to the world of *Go Vegan* guilt-free desserts! All the recipes you will find in this section have passed the test with discerning dessert aficionados. Most people are seekers of sugar. The 'sweet' taste receptor is right there on the tip of the tongue and cries out for satisfaction. I want to show you how to satisfy this craving with healthy treats.

These desserts use only natural organic ingredients and have great nutritional value. Some of the recipes are for everyday enjoyment, such as the apple sauce, the kanten or a few adzuki bites; others are for special occasions. The day-to-day recipes are doable even on a low budget. Bill and I personally enjoy the more simple desserts, but when we have family and friends for dinner it is great to make something special.

It's important to note, however, that if weight is an issue, you should be aware that the richer desserts are more calorically dense than the lighter choices.

I only use organic fair-trade ingredients that are kind to the soil and the planet and do not involve food slavery. Please be conscious of where your ingredients come from.

- Gingered Apple Sauce with Cashew Cream and Crunchy Granola
- Mum's Black and White Chocolate Cake
- Peach Kanten with Sweet Date Cream
- Chocolate Adzuki Bites
- Sweet Cherry Ice Cream with Chocolate Sauce
- Oatmeal Walnut Cookies
- Lemon Tart
- Mini Orange Chocolate Pots
- The Sweet Nosh Bar
- Choc Chip and Raisin Cookies
- Carrot Cake with Lemon Frosting

Gingered Apple Sauce with Cashew Cream and Crunchy Granola

Apple sauce can be made with peeled apples and a variety of spices. Flavourings or sweeteners such as rice syrup or cinnamon are also commonly added. It's our absolute favourite dessert, straight from my jars. I only make the toppings when we have guests. Bill and I have very simple tastes.

For the apple sauce

4 organic apples
2 tbsp apple juice
Pinch of sea salt
1 tsp freshly squeezed ginger juice

Toppings

Cashew cream
Granola (page 48)
Fresh apple slices

For the cashew cream

1 cup cashews, soaked overnight
Filtered water
2 medjool dates
½ tsp vanilla extract

Drain the cashews and rinse with cold water. Transfer to a blender, and add the dates and vanilla extract. Pour in half a cup of cold filtered water. Blend on high for 2 to 3 minutes, until very smooth and creamy. Add more water if necessary. Cover and refrigerate until ready to use. The cream will thicken as it sits.

Wash and peel the fruit, remove the cores and slice them into bite-sized chunks. Place in a pot with a little filtered water or apple juice, and add a pinch of sea salt. Simmer covered on a very low heat until the fruit is soft. When the apples are cooked, either mash with a potato masher or blend to a cream with an upright or stick blender. Stir in the fresh ginger juice and serve this delicious and easy dessert topped with some cashew cream, crunchy granola and a slice of apple. Makes 8 servings.

Note – This dessert is a daily staple in our home. It's super for taking the edge of any sugar cravings you may experience. Apples are a high-fibre, low-calorie snack that are extremely rich in important antioxidant flavonoids and dietary fibre. The phytonutrients and antioxidants in apples may help reduce the risk of developing cancer, hypertension, diabetes and heart disease.

An important part of ecology is how we treat the living world which is the source of our existence. The solution to all our environmental problems is based on one simple idea – respect life. Most of our attitudes about the web of life that supports us were formed centuries ago. Sometimes those ideas were driven by necessity, and often by superstition. Over time, superstitions translate into mythologies that feed habits of thought and action. The use of animals for food, clothing and entertainment demonstrates that we have not considered what this habit says about our understanding of life itself. Animals are sentient, which means they have feelings. They want to live, they feel pain and have relationships with each other that demonstrate kinship and even empathy. We have no need to impose suffering and death simply to satisfy our own pleasure.

Mum's Black and White Chocolate Cake

I created this cake for my mum's 90th birthday. The crunchy base texture contrasts with the creamy topping to make this sumptuous cake irresistible. It's my students' and clients' 'go-to' special-occasion cake. The same base is used in the lemon tart. You only need to learn both toppings and you have two amazing cakes for special occasions.

Oat or quinoa nut crust

- 1 cup oat or quinoa flour
- 2 cups pecans
- 2 tbsp ground flax
- ½ tsp ground cinnamon
- ¼ tsp sea salt
- ¼ cup brown rice syrup

Preheat the oven to 180°C (350°F), gas 4. Put 2 cups of pecans in a food processor and process until they start to clump, and oils start to release. Transfer the pecan mixture into a large bowl and mix with the rest of the ingredients, except the rice syrup. In a small saucepan warm the brown rice syrup to reduce its viscosity. Pour into the mixture and mix well. Using your hands, squeeze the dough over and over to combine. You should be able to form a ball with it. If it's too dry, add a little water. Transfer the pecan dough into a 9 inch push-up fluted flan dish and smooth out evenly. Press down firmly with your fingers, bringing it up along the sides, pressing as firmly as you can. Prick the dough with a fork to make a cross. Bake for 10–12 minutes until slightly golden. Remove from the oven and allow to cool on a wire rack.

For the cake topping

- 1½ cups cashew nuts, soaked overnight
- 1 cup almond milk
- 2 tbsp agar flakes
- 3 heaped tbsp kuzu, mixed in 4 tbsp filtered water
- ½ cup maple syrup or rice syrup
- 1 tbsp vanilla extract
- 2 tbsp lemon juice
- Cocoa powder for dusting
- Fresh raspberries for garnish

Drain the cashews, rinse in cold water and put in a high-speed blender, then set aside. Put the plant-based milk into a small saucepan and sprinkle in the agar flakes. Leave for a few minutes to allow the agar flakes to be absorbed. Set the flame to medium low and add the kuzu mixture, stirring constantly to avoid the kuzu lumping. When slightly simmering and thickened, remove from the heat and pour into the blender. Add all the other ingredients, except the cocoa powder, and whizz until smooth. Pour over the cooled cake base and leave to sit for 10 minutes. Sprinkle with the cocoa powder and place in the refrigerator. Once set, decorate with fresh raspberries. Makes 8 servings.

Note – Cashews are used throughout the world, as paste base for curries in India and Sri Lanka, as whole nuts in Thailand and China, and brewed as sweeteners in Spanish and South American desserts. Add them to chocolates and cakes. Please ensure you purchase fair-trade organic cashews grown using sustainable farming practices, such as multi-cropping and practices promoting biodiversity.

Peach Kanten with Sweet Date Cream

Kanten is a Japanese dessert that is somewhat likened to jelly or Jell-O. It is made with agar-agar, a gelatinous substance that comes from several species of dried seaweeds. It's a macrobiotic classic dessert. Deliciously simple, and simply delicious, this healthy dessert is also packed with the natural fibre found in agar flakes.

Kanten
6 sweet ripe peaches
3 medjool dates, pits removed
1 cup apple juice
3 tbsp agar flakes
Pinch sea salt

Topping
Sweet date cream
Fresh blueberries
Sprig fresh mint for garnish

Sweet date cream
½ cup cashews, soaked overnight
4 tbsp almond milk or filtered water
3 medjool dates, pitted
¼ tsp lemon juice
¼ tsp vanilla

Drain the cashews and place all of the ingredients for the cream in a high-speed blender. Blend until creamy. You may have to stop and scrape down the sides of the blender with a spatula a few times.

To remove the skins of the peaches easily, soak them in boiling filtered water for 30 seconds then transfer to an ice bath. Remove the skins and stones from the peaches and transfer the flesh to a blender.

When blended you will have around 3 cups of puréed peaches. Add the dates to the blender. In a small saucepan bring the apple juice, agar flakes and sea salt to a boil, reduce to low and simmer for 5 minutes, stirring occasionally. Pour into the blender and blend to a creamy consistency. Divide into individual serving dishes and chill in the fridge to set. Top with some sweet date cream and fresh berries. Garnish with a sprig of fresh mint. Makes 4–6 servings.

Note – This delicious kanten can be made using many other seasonal fruits – watermelon, strawberries, etc. – simply use a quantity that will give you 3 cups of puréed fruit.

T. Colin Campbell published *The China Study* in 2005. It is a 'must read' for anyone who wants to understand the science behind a healthy vegan approach to eating. Professor Campbell's life's work had been dedicated to understanding the relationship between diet and disease, particularly cancer. His work with government agencies and Cornell University has embraced both laboratory and epidemiological study. *The China Study* is the single most important book that has driven public acceptance of a plant-based diet. Part of his work has focused on the way that casein, a protein found in cow's milk, can actually stimulate cancer growth, and how a plant-based diet can kill cancer cells. There are so many plant-based milks to choose from. Whatever you desire, I can offer you a plant-based alternative.

Chocolate Adzuki Bites

Why adzuki beans for dessert? Apart from tasting amazing, adzuki beans (also known as red beans) are high in protein and fibre. They are a low-fat plant food rich in calcium, phosphorus and magnesium. Their soluble fibre can help to stabilise cholesterol levels, improve digestive health and keep you feeling full for longer. All my clients and students love them.

1 cup cooked adzuki beans (see adzuki bean soup, page 64)
1 cup pecans
8 medjool dates, stones removed
3 tbsp cocoa powder
¼ tsp vanilla extract
Desiccated coconut for rolling

Blend all the ingredients (except the coconut) in a food processor until you achieve a creamy texture. You may have to stop and push the mixture down with your spatula a few times. Take heaped teaspoons and roll into balls. Drop the balls into a bowl filled with the coconut and shake until well covered. Chill in the refrigerator for a few hours and enjoy. They also freeze well. Truly scrumptious and healthy. Makes 24 balls.

In many cultures the concept of 'cause and effect' is honoured as a rule of nature. This is a practical idea and not at all mysterious. Everything we do has effects that ripple out into the world and rebound on our health and well-being. We often think that we can fool karma because the results of actions are not immediate. Think of all the foods we know are harmful but continue to eat. We may know that dairy and sugar are poor health choices, but we continue to eat them because we do not see the immediate effects. Over time blocked sinuses or inflamed joints may be the reward, but we don't associate the cause and the effect. 'As you sow, so shall you reap.' The best way to test this is to simply eat our Human Ecology Diet for several months and see how you feel. The information contained within the Human Ecology Diet chapter at the end of the book covers all you need to know about how to replace the harmful foods with healthy ones.

Sweet Cherry Ice Cream with Chocolate Sauce

There are two general varieties of cherries: sweet and sour. Cherry and chocolate are not a new or revolutionary flavour combination, but when beautiful organic sweet cherries are used alongside a little chocolate sauce, the ice cream turns into something deliciously decadent.

2 cups banana, sliced
2 cups frozen sweet cherries
2 tbsp plant-based milk
¼ tsp vanilla extract
Fresh mint sprig for garnish

Peel and slice the banana and freeze in a freezer bag overnight. Remove from the bag and allow the banana to sit on the counter top for a few minutes before processing. Place all the ingredients into a food processor or high-speed blender. Pulse and push the fruit back down to the blade. Process until thick and creamy. Makes 4–6 servings.

Note – If using a blender, start slowly then increase the speed, using the tamper to push down the frozen fruit. You may have to add an extra few tablespoons of plant-based milk or water to the blender. Increase the speed to high, continue to use the tamper, pushing the ingredients down to the blade. Blend until you reach a thick and creamy texture. You can add other berries and frozen fruits for wonderful colour and a different taste. Serve immediately with some fresh fruit and/or with the chocolate sauce. Garnish with a sprig of fresh mint.

Quick chocolate sauce
¼ cup rice syrup
3 tbsp cocoa powder
½ tsp vanilla extract or powder

In a small bowl, mix all the ingredients together. Pour into a squeezy bottle and use as a decorative treat for ice cream or other desserts. Keep refrigerated.

Oatmeal Walnut Cookies

These are a really wholesome treat, lower in fat and sugar than most shop-bought biscuits and packed with oatmeal and raisins for extra nutrients and flavour. Many of my cookies incorporate fruit and spices, rather than extra sugar and fat. I decided to share this recipe as it is Bill's absolute favourite.

1½ cups oatmeal
¾ cup wholewheat pastry flour
¾ cup unbleached white flour or almond flour
1 tsp baking powder
¼ tsp sea salt
¾ cup currants
1 cup walnuts, toasted and coarsely chopped
2 tbsp apple butter
½ cup barley malt or brown rice syrup
Zest of 1 orange
½ cup orange juice
1 tbsp finely grated fresh ginger juice
1 tsp vanilla

Preheat the oven to 180°C (350°F), gas 4. Line two baking trays with parchment paper. In a large bowl, mix the dry ingredients. In a smaller bowl, whisk together the wet ingredients and then stir into the dry ingredients. Transfer heaping tablespoons of dough to the baking sheet, leaving at least 1 inch (2 cm) of space between the cookies. Flatten the cookies with the back of a fork to make rounds. Dip the fork in water to keep the mixture from sticking. Bake the cookies until the edges and undersides are golden, 25 to 30 minutes. Remove from the oven and allow to cool on a rack. Makes 16–18 cookies.

Note – Apple butter is a highly concentrated form of apple sauce produced by long, slow cooking of apples with cider or water to a point where the sugar in the apples caramelises, turning the apple butter a deep brown. The concentration of sugar gives apple butter a much longer shelf life as a preserve than apple sauce.

 When you start cooking my recipes you will see that I always recommend a diet of wholefoods that is low in simple sugars and includes lots of fresh vegetables, greens and healthy fats, as well as plenty filtered water. Many new vegan products are hitting the market, from ready-made meals to desserts. Don't rely on them for a good diet. They often contain excessive amounts of salt, hydrogenated oils and other refined ingredients. Processed foods wreak havoc with the digestive system and can cause acid indigestion, bloating, gas and constipation. Plus, they can rob the body of magnesium. When you cook your own food, you are in charge of what goes into it. The difference can be like night and day in terms of not only taste but your health.

Lemon Tart

This lemon tart is a lovely conclusion to an elegant dinner! I spent quite a bit of time trying every sort of lemon tart imaginable. Creating the right texture and taste was my goal.

I came up with this version. A rich buttery crust with just the right amount of filling. The crust is the same as in the black and white chocolate cake.

Oat or quinoa nut crust

   1 cup oat or quinoa flour
   2 cups pecans
   2 tbsp ground flax
   ½ tsp ground cinnamon
   ¼ tsp sea salt
   ¼ cup brown rice syrup

Preheat the oven to 180°C (350°F), gas 4. Put 2 cups of pecans into a food processor and process until they start to clump, and oils start to release. Transfer the pecan mixture into a large bowl and mix with the rest of the ingredients, except the rice syrup. In a small saucepan, warm the brown rice syrup to reduce its viscosity. Pour into the mixture and mix well. Using your hands, squeeze the dough over and over to combine. You should be able to form a ball with it. If it's too dry, add a little water. Transfer the pecan dough into a 9 inch push-up fluted flan dish and smooth out evenly. Press down firmly with your fingers, bringing it up along the sides and pressing as firmly as you can. Prick the dough with a fork to make a cross. Bake for 10–12 minutes until slightly golden. Remove from the oven and allow to cool on a wire rack.

Filling

   ¾ cup 180 ml unsweetened organic
      coconut cream
   ⅓ cup fresh lemon juice
   ½ tbsp lemon zest
   1 cup maple syrup or rice syrup
   ½ tbsp agar flakes
   2 tbsp kuzu, mixed into ¼ cup filtered
      water
   Desiccated coconut

Whisk the coconut cream, lemon juice, zest, maple syrup and agar flakes together in a saucepan. In a small bowl, mix the kuzu and water to form a paste. Add the kuzu mixture to the pan and heat on a low flame until slightly simmering, stirring constantly to avoid lumping. Once the mixture has thickened, take off the heat and leave to cool for 1–2 minutes, then pour into the prepared tart base. Sprinkle with desiccated coconut and leave to cool. Once at room temperature, cover and place in the fridge for at least 2 hours, or until ready to serve. I prefer to leave overnight. Cut into slices and serve as is or with some fresh sweet strawberries, in season. Makes 8 servings.

Mini Orange Chocolate Pots

A luscious dessert, with a dash of tangy orange. This recipe is really easy to make and provides a truly divine result, especially when served with fresh orange slices. I recommend leaving the chocolate pots in the fridge overnight to chill, but the recipe could easily be made on the day.

120 g bar 100% cocoa chocolate
300 g pack organic silken tofu
¼ cup maple syrup
¼ cup rice milk
1 tsp lemon juice
1 heaped tbsp tahini
¼ tsp pure orange extract
¼ tsp vanilla extract

To serve
Fresh orange slices
Desiccated coconut for garnish

Put a small amount of boiling filtered water in a saucepan. Place a metal bowl on top of the pan. Break the chocolate into pieces in the metal bowl and stir until melted. Remove from the heat. In a blender, purée all of the ingredients to a cream. Divide into small cups and chill in the refrigerator until set. Serve with a few fresh orange slices and garnish desiccated coconut. Makes 6 servings.

Note – The organic long-life tofu that I use is made with just three ingredients: organic whole soya beans; spring water from Mount Fuji; and nigari, a naturally occurring mineral-rich coagulant derived from seawater. Denser and richer than other soft tofu, it has a silky soft, smooth texture, whilst maintaining firmness. Protein-rich and low in fat, this tofu is a staple in my cooking classes. I use it in creamy sauces and desserts, and it makes the best tofu scramble ever.

The Sweet Nosh Bar

Aptly named after this category, my sweet nosh bar has been tried and tested many times. Bill was delighted when I was finally happy to move on to the next recipe. He tasted way too many of them and was delighted to return to his daily staple of our favourite apple sauce. This is a great recipe that works well as a super party snack – hence why I have used larger quantities. Kids also love making them. Reduce the ingredients to suit your requirements. These bars last for weeks in a sealed container and also freeze well.

    3 cups rolled oats
    16 medjool dates, pitted
    2 cup pecans, almonds or walnuts
    ½ cup chocolate chips
    ½ cup almond or peanut butter
    ½ cup brown rice syrup
    ¼ cup shelled hemp
    ¼ cup pumpkin seeds

Preheat the oven to 180°C (350°F), gas 4. Place the oats on a baking sheet and toast for 15–20 minutes, or until golden brown. Place the dates, nuts and chocolate chips in the food processor. Pulse until broken down into a sticky consistency. Transfer to a large bowl and add the toasted oats, shelled hemp and pumpkin seeds. Melt almond or peanut butter with the rice syrup in a saucepan over a low heat. Stir into the mixture and, using your hands, squeeze to form a cohesive dough. Line an 8 × 8 inch (20 × 20 cm) square baking dish with parchment paper. Press the mixture into the dish and flatten with your hands. Cover and place in the fridge for 20–30 minutes to set. Remove by placing a plate on top and inverting the set mixture onto a chopping board. Slice into bite-sized bars. Makes 32 bars.

Food additives are most often used to disguise the quality of the food we eat. They make the food taste, smell and look different than it really is. There are thousands of chemical substances that are added to processed foods. Some of these chemicals are naturally found in foods or have been used as flavouring or preserving agents for centuries; most have not. Our bodies have never encountered them through the process of evolution, certainly not in the concentrations or combinations that we find in the supermarket. If an ingredient has more than three syllables it is probably best left on the shelf. Eat whole, natural foods. Your body knows what to do with them. Why should you be part of the experiment?

Choc Chip and Raisin Cookies

For decades, I have been creating lots of healthy cookie recipes for our students' snacks when running our workshops. Both children and adults will love these crisp and chewy, melt-in-the-mouth cookies. You don't need to sacrifice nutrition to give yourself or your family a treat. These cookies travel well to school or the office.

  3 cups blanched almond flour
  ¼ tsp sea salt
  ½ tsp bicarbonate of soda
  ½ cup chopped pecans or other nuts (optional)
  ¼ cup grain-sweetened chocolate chips
  ¼ cup raisins
  1 tbsp apple butter
  ½ cup rice or maple syrup
  1 tsp vanilla extract

Preheat the oven to 180°C (350°F), gas 4. Line two baking sheets with parchment paper. Combine the dry ingredients in a medium bowl. In a smaller bowl stir together the wet ingredients, and then stir into the dry ingredients. Put tablespoons of dough on the baking sheet, leaving at least 1 inch (2 cm) of space between them. Flatten the spoons of dough with the back of a fork to make them round. Dip the fork in water to keep the mixture from sticking. Bake for 10 minutes, or until golden. Cool on a baking rack and serve. The blanched almond flour gives these cookies a delicious 'buttery' taste. Makes 16 cookies.

Carrot Cake with Lemon Frosting

This is a great carrot cake recipe that is easy to make. Walnuts add a lovely crunch, but feel free to leave them out if you don't like nuts. You will love this incredibly moist carrot cake recipe with ultra-creamy lemon frosting.

Dry ingredients

1 cup plain flour
1 cup wholemeal pastry flour
1 tsp ground cinnamon
½ tsp fine sea salt
½ tsp ground nutmeg
2 tsp baking powder
2 tsp baking soda

Wet ingredients

½ cup raisins
½ cup freshly squeezed orange juice
1 cup maple syrup
1 tbsp apple butter
½ cup oat or soy milk
½ tsp vanilla extract
2 tsp apple cider vinegar
2 cups grated carrots, firmly packed
½ cup walnuts, chopped

Frosting

2 cups cashews, soaked overnight
2 tbsp lemon juice
Pinch sea salt
1 cup maple or rice syrup
½ tsp ume plum seasoning
1 tsp vanilla extract

Topping

Chopped toasted walnuts
Pomegranate seeds

Drain the cashews and discard the soaking water. Add all of the frosting ingredients to a food processor or blender and blend until silky smooth. Transfer to a covered dish and chill in the refrigerator. Cut two 8 inch (20 cm) circles from parchment paper and line the bottoms of two round cake tins. Soak the raisins in the orange juice for 15 minutes. Preheat the oven to 170°C (340°F), gas 4.

Using a sieve, add all of the dry ingredients to a large bowl. Drain the raisins and place two tablespoons of the orange juice into a small bowl with the apple butter, maple or rice syrup, oat or soy milk, vanilla and vinegar. Mix well, then pour into the dry mixture, along with the raisins and carrots, and stir to mix. Fold in the walnuts. Divide the mixture between the two cake tins.

Place in the centre of the oven and bake for 30 minutes. Remove from the oven and cool the cake tins on a wire rack before inverting each one on to a plate. Remove the pans, peel off the parchment paper and cool completely on a wire rack. Spread a generous layer of frosting on the top of one of the sponges. Pop the other layer on top, spread the remaining frosting on top and, if you desire, around the sponge. Decorate with the toasted walnut pieces and pomegranate seeds. Chill in the refrigerator and slice when ready to enjoy. Makes 8 servings.

Note – Cook one or two more sponges to make a three- or four-layered cake.

Our bodies show us what we should be eating. If we found a new animal in the jungle, one never before seen, one of the first questions we would ask would be 'What does it eat?' Knowing what an animal eats gives you great insight into its true nature and how it has survived. It gives insight into what its habits are and how it relates to its environment. The one aspect of any animal that clearly defines what it has eaten is the digestive system. Everything from the mouth to the intestines will reflect its dietary history. When we look at humans this way, the facts are astounding.

We have teeth that are only adapted for grinding and cutting, not tearing, these are herbivore characteristics. Our saliva is devised to digest carbohydrate and our stomach has only one-tenth of the acid of a carnivore. Our intestines are clearly intended for the digestion of plant matter and not meat. We have simply been sold a vision of human evolution that is contradicted by biological fact.

Fruit and vegetables have often racked up thousands of **air miles** before they reach you. The case for regional and seasonal eating is commonly based on food waste and the environmental effect of food transportation, both serious issues that should be included in any discussion of human nutrition. The world of international food distribution is a topsy-turvy, costly and wasteful exercise. Cod caught off Norway is shipped to China to be turned into fillets, then shipped back to Norway for sale. Argentine lemons fill supermarket shelves on the Citrus Coast of Spain, while local lemons rot on the ground.

You may have noticed that there is a time of year between the height of summer and the onset of autumn that is almost a distinct season, late summer. It often is a period following a heavy frost when the apparent onset of autumn reverses and it becomes warm again. In the Far East this time of year was seen to have special attributes and corresponded with the harvest of many food crops used during the colder months of autumn and winter. Some of the crops, such as sweet varieties of squash, sweet root vegetables like carrots and parsnips, and maize, are thought to be very important to eat in this season. These are naturally sweet foods, especially when baked to bring out the natural sweetness. These foods are thought to be strengthening to the immune functions of the body and the pancreas.

Teas and Macrobiotic Home Remedies

I have taken one or two recipes from my book *Macrobiotics for all Seasons* to share with you here. I am hugely passionate about these teas and remedies that I see aiding in the healing of so many of my clients' health issues. Enjoy them also as a refreshing beverage or whenever you feel you need a pick-me-up or have overindulged during the holiday season.

Hippocrates, the father of Western medicine, claimed that food was the most important factor in healing. His most common advice to patients was that they eat a simple plant-based diet and get regular exercise. This approach was driven by his observation that disease was most often created by personal health habits. He said that illnesses do not come upon us by accident but are the result of small daily actions. I refer to this as dying from your 'whole life's choices'. As Hippocrates said, 'The natural healing force within each of us daily is the greatest force in getting better.' It is ironic that the acknowledged 'father' of modern medicine would be considered a practitioner of alternative medicine today.

- Immune Booster – Magic Mineral Broth
- Digestive Aid – Ume Sho Kuzu
- Kidney Tonic – Adzuki Bean Tea
- Chlorophyll Tea – Parsley and Coriander Drink
- Fat Buster – Dried Shiitake and Dried Daikon

Ume sho kuzu

Magic mineral
broth

Parsley and
coriander drink

Adzuki bean tea

Dried shiitake and
dried daikon

Immune Booster – Magic Mineral Broth

I recently wrote this article for T. Colin Campbell's Nutrition Studies website. It was in response to the bone broth fad doing yet another round of why we should drink the bones of animals.

Soups and broths have been a regular feature in cooking since before historical records. In fact, one of the oldest books in Chinese medicine is Dr Yi Yin's soup classic. In the West we can look to Hippocrates, the father of Western medicine. He was fond of recommending barley soup to his patients. What we know is that for a person who is ill, it may be easier to drink a restorative soup than eat a full meal. Soups have been used for many reasons.

The bone broth fad, which consists of boiling animal bones and tissue as a strengthening tonic, is a little strange for a number of reasons. A number of nutritional studies show that animal-sourced fats and proteins are harmful to health. Heavy metals and other toxic compounds ingested by animals – including those raised for food – have a tendency to accumulate in fatty tissue.

The history of boiling bones and other tissues that are difficult to eat undoubtedly began as a way of gleaning every possible bit of nutrition from the body of animals killed for food – either hunted or farmed – in times of food shortages.

In my experience, whole, nutritious vegetables are all that's needed for some of the most healing and restorative soups and broths you can make. The broth below is a favourite with my clients. It contains ingredients that are energising and extremely nutritious. Three ingredients in the broth may be unfamiliar to some readers. They are foods that are used in the traditions of China and Japan and have some fascinating qualities. As a long-time teacher and health counsellor of macrobiotics, I use these fantastic ingredients in many of my soups and broths.

Kombu seaweed

According to Professor Arasaki of the University of Tokyo, sea vegetables contain more minerals than any other food. All the 56 elements essential for human health are present in sea vegetables, including many trace minerals that are often lacking in modern produce owing to demineralisation of the soil. This may be why the people of Okinawa seldom show signs of mineral depletion and live long lives.

Scientists at McGill University in Canada have shown that sodium alginate – one of the chemical compounds found in kombu – removes radioactive elements and heavy metals from the system.

Shiitake mushrooms

Shiitake mushrooms are well known for their use in traditional medicine. Among the many mushrooms that have been tested for unique chemical properties, they have always stood out. In 1936, Dr Kisaku Mori established the Institute of Mushroom Research in Tokyo. Until his death in 1977, he worked with scientists from around the world to document the medicinal effects of shiitake.

Mori's work gained significant attention, particularly in Japanese medicinal circles, and beginning in the 1960s, scientists launched an extensive research effort to uncover the secret of shiitake mushrooms' legendary healing powers. Their studies – about one hundred of them – all focused on shiitake mushrooms' ability to rapidly lower serum cholesterol, as well as its potent antitumour, antiviral and antibiotic properties.

Shiitake mushrooms were also found to have antifungal and antioxidant properties, and to reduce toxicity in the liver.

Magic mineral broth recipe

I offer all my clients and students a big cup of my fabulous broth at all my classes and workshops. I also keep this broth on hand as a soup stock.

A vegetable broth made from organically grown vegetables can be an excellent source of essential electrolytes. Ionic minerals are the key to maintaining good health. The broth is a wonderful, filling snack that will also provide you with many healthy nutrients that will help you feel great. The recipe can be varied to suit your taste.

I use my magic broth for clients with a host of illnesses. It's also fantastic for discharging excess fat and proteins that accumulate around our organs, so it is a wonderful broth for weight loss. Please incorporate this amazing broth into your diet. A healthy equilibrium is the key to strength and vitality. You can make this broth along with me in your kitchen by visiting this web page: https://www.youtube.com/watch?v=zxVu-WAPHTg.

    2 × 5 inch (12 cm) strips of dried kombu seaweed
    6 dried shiitake mushrooms
    40 g pack of dried daikon
    6 carrots, cut into chunks
    2 medium onions, cut into chunks
    1 leek, white and green parts, cut into chunks
    1 small bunch of celery, including the heart, cut into chunks
    5 unpeeled cloves garlic, halved
    1 small pumpkin or squash with skin on, quartered

5 inch (12 cm) piece of fresh ginger, sliced
4 cups chopped greens, such as kale, chard
½ bunch fresh flat-leaf parsley

In a large stock or soup pot, combine all of the ingredients. Fill the pot to 2 inches (5 cm) below the rim with filtered water, cover and bring to a boil. Remove the lid, decrease the heat to medium low and simmer for a minimum of 2 hours. As the stock simmers, some of the water will evaporate; add more if the vegetables are exposed. Simmer until the full richness of the vegetables can be tasted. Strain the stock and pour into glass storage jars. Refrigerating works well with any broth.

The ingredients above serve a family for days, but you require rather a large stock/soup pot, so adjust the ingredients accordingly for your own needs. Drink 2 to 3 cups daily in between meals.

Digestive Aid – Ume Sho Kuzu

This is one of the most widely recommended macrobiotic home remedies. It is made from kuzu, a gigantic root that is bigger than an average man, typically growing to about 100 kg per root. It is widely used in both traditional Japanese and Chinese medicine. Umeboshi (a pickled sour plum) and shoyu (natural soy sauce) create a magical combination.

I use kuzu remedies for many of my clients to relieve digestive problems, including heartburn, poor digestion, flatulence, abdominal ache, intestinal irritation, sickness, diarrhoea and IBS.

It is a wonderful drink to take before and after travelling on a long-haul flight, or if you feel you are coming down with a cold.

1 tsp kuzu
1 umeboshi plum
Few drops shoyu
Few drops fresh ginger juice
Filtered water

Mash the flesh of the umeboshi plum with a small teaspoon. In a small saucepan, bring one cup of water and the plum (including the stone) to the boil over a medium heat. Dissolve the kuzu in 2 tablespoons of cold filtered water and add to the pot. Stir constantly to prevent lumps. Cook until the mixture becomes translucent. Add four or five drops of shoyu and a little grated ginger juice. You can cook up a larger batch and reheat.

Kidney Tonic – Adzuki Bean Tea

This tea is great for strengthening the kidneys and bladder. Adzuki beans help balance blood sugar levels by relaxing the pancreas and spleen. You will note that I have used these amazing beans in soups and desserts in my cookbook. Versatility reigns supreme with plants, so it's time to 'spill the beans' and make some of this wonderful tonic.

    1 cup adzuki beans
    3 inch (7 cm) piece of kombu seaweed
    4 cups filtered water
    Splash shoyu

Place the beans and kombu in a pot and cover with the water. Allow to soak overnight. Bring to a boil then lower the flame, cover and simmer for approximately 20–30 minutes.

Strain out the beans and drink the liquid while hot. You may continue cooking the beans for longer with additional water until soft and edible for regular consumption. Several cups of adzuki bean tea can be taken during the day to speed weight loss.

Chlorophyll Tea – Parsley and Coriander Drink

This is of one of my favourite teas, which I suggest to all my students and clients to incorporate into their lives. Literally in a few minutes you have this chlorophyll-rich detox drink. These greens assist the body in ridding itself of toxic metals. It also helps with intestinal gas. Drink this tea after meals.

    Few sprigs parsley leaves
    Few sprigs coriander leaves

Put the leaves into a mug and add hot filtered water. Allow to infuse for 2–3 minutes. Drink the tea and eat the greens.

Fat Buster – Dried Shiitake and Dried Daikon

This drink is excellent for helping the liver release the fats stored during the winter and helps in any weight-loss programme. You should have a cup of this tea once or twice a day, preferably between meals. You may notice that your urine has a strong smell or changes colour when drinking these teas – don't be alarmed.

    1 large or two small dried shiitake mushrooms
    ½ cup dried daikon
    3 cups spring water

Place the shiitake and dried daikon in a small pot and cover with the water. Leave to soak for about 20 minutes. Slice the shiitake, discard the stem and add the sliced cap back into the pot. Bring to a boil covered, then reduce the heat and simmer for about 15–20 minutes. Remove and discard the vegetables. Drink the tea while hot.

Note – You can also add some leafy green vegetables, such as watercress, at the end. Simmer for a further 2 to 3 minutes. I quite often serve this as a consommé if the meal I am serving is a little rich and heavier than normal.

The Human Ecology Diet
Nutrition for the Future
by Bill Tara

Since the 1960s I have been involved in a revolution. It is a revolution that began underground as a loose collection of 'health food' enthusiasts, students of Asian philosophy, nature lovers, rebellious doctors and nutritionists, and people who had experienced incredible health recoveries through changing their diets. It was a rag-tag army. It was ridiculed, scoffed at and sometimes labelled as dangerous. Strangely, it kept growing.

The major goals of this revolution were various but related:

- To acknowledge food as a primary factor in health and healing
- To recognise the fact that the food industry is creating unhealthy food and needs to change
- To admit that our methods of farming and animal agriculture need radical change to meet environmental and health standards
- To appreciate that animals are sentient creatures and not a source of human food.

What has taken place over the last 50 years would have seemed astounding to many. Millions of individuals and families have started eating lower on the food chain and attempting to eat locally and seasonally. Nutritional science is moving towards 'plant-based diets'. Veganism is increasing at a phenomenal rate, particularly among the young, and the harmful effects of animal agriculture are now accepted as fact. This is all good news, but unfortunately not enough.

The junk-food industry has found new markets in emerging economies. Around the world the fast food industry is being sold regardless of social and environmental impact. The power of big business is more active than ever in influencing government policy, and many in the medical profession cling to what was taught in the 1950s as food science. There is an urgent need for new life to be introduced into the conversation about our social ideas and ideals about food. The work is not done.

The application of Western science to nutrition began in earnest in the late eighteenth century, but did not gain its present focus until the mid 1800s. Before that, there had certainly developed a sophisticated understanding of the importance of a healthy diet in many parts of the world, but most in the West would have considered those to be 'primitive' approaches to the topic.

The cultures of India, Greece, China and Japan, as well as many indigenous cultures around the world, had created food wisdom for health and healing over many centuries. These systems were founded on observation and accumulated folk wisdom, written down or passed on through oral tradition. These were the studies of whole, natural foods with little or no processing. Many of these traditions are reflected in our Human Ecology Diet.

This is particularly true of macrobiotics, a philosophy and dietary practice introduced to the West by the Japanese philosopher George Ohsawa. He introduced his teachings to America in the 1950s. His work was carried on by his most eminent student, Michio Kushi. Kushi was a major force for the development of the natural-foods industry and cultural awareness of food as a key to health and healing in America and Western Europe.

Macrobiotic dietary principles have been constantly developing over the past six decades through the experience of practitioners and the thousands of individuals and families who apply this way of eating in their daily life.

The philosophy of Asian medicine as practised in China and Japan forms the inspiration for macrobiotic practice. These concepts reflect physical, environmental and social observations from a period of over 5,000 years. On the surface, the philosophy bears little relationship to Western nutritional science, yet the conclusions are remarkably similar.

Macrobiotics is a way of understanding the effects of different foods and making choices according to individual and social needs. Michio Kushi developed the Standard Diet in the early 1980s with assistance from myself, Edward Esko, William Spear and Murray Snyder.

The Standard Diet was presented to offer a general model of macrobiotic eating. The model was helpful to the growing number of people seeking help with their health, who were dealing with cancer, heart disease and a variety of serious illnesses.

Since macrobiotics is not a set diet but a 'philosophy of eating', it has fostered a variety of interpretations over the past decade. Teachers and health counsellors now recommend an assortment of dietary practices. In some cases, it has become difficult to identify specifically what the term 'macrobiotic' really means. The meaning may vary from country to country. We have labelled the diet described in this book the 'Human Ecology Diet' so that there is complete clarity.

Our approach is firmly based on macrobiotic principles, but also reflects our personal experience with clients and students, the newest discoveries in nutritional science, ecological concerns and vegan ethics. We wanted to be clear with our intentions. A more complete explanation of our dietary principles can be seen in my book, *Eat Right and Save The Planet*.

Many of the problems that face modern society are a direct result of our failure to forge a respectful attitude towards life itself. This gap in human thought and action is reflected most dramatically in the way we use the resources of nature in our daily lives. One of the most commonly ignored elements of this misuse is our relationship with the food we eat.

The modern diet is the direct cause of the rise of degenerative diseases such as heart disease, cancer, diabetes and stroke in the affluent countries of the world. It is also a primary cause of increased pollution of the environment by the inefficient and harmful practices of animal agriculture, in particular. All this damage is done in concert with the senseless killing of billions of animals. The combination of these factors is a sad comment on our collective consciousness.

Governments, the medical profession and industry have shown unwillingness to address this issue in a meaningful way. If this situation is to be changed for the better, it will take urgent action in the arena of public education that leads to a shift in consumption patterns.

This education is not dependent on increased scientific research; the factual data is already there. What is required is effective communication of the facts combined with practical strategies for applying them. Individuals and families need the life skills that can improve their personal health while knowing that they are also contributing to environmental sustainability and social justice.

If we look at the leading edge of nutritional science, we see that there is little disagreement. Certainly, there are conflicts with those who stubbornly defend the past, have a vested interest in a particular product or refuse to believe that the foods they love can possibly be harmful. These arguments are commercial or emotional, but do not conform to facts or logic.

The Human Ecology Diet is guided by the principle that nutrition is a much broader study than the chemical composition of the foods we eat. Nutrition represents our attitudes about health, the environment, society and the natural world. It encompasses the growing, processing, packaging and distribution of food items.

The remarkable thing is that when foods damage one aspect of the web of life they damage the total fabric. This is not a mystical formula, it is a reflection of ecological process.

The foods we commonly use are not 'superfoods' packed with powerful and mysterious micronutrients. In fact, a healthy diet is more a fusion of traditional diets from around the world with the simple considerations of ethical, ecological and economic realities taken into account. These foods are low in calories and nutrient-dense. They are foods that reduce nutritional stress, since they are particularly suited to feeding a healthy gut biome, and are easy to digest, assimilate and metabolise.

Human Health

The modern diet was developed largely in America and then spread into Europe and around the globe. The modern diet is filled with manufactured foods with extremely high concentrations of animal protein, fat, refined sugars and chemical additives. This diet has been cited in scientific literature over the past 50 years as one of the major causes of obesity, many cancers, heart disease, diabetes and stroke.

The World Health Organization estimates that between 60% and 75% of degenerative disease can be prevented. The primary causes are smoking and diet. The statistical basis of these phenomena is irrefutable, and yet governments have not shown the courage or leadership to challenge the international food industry or demand more rigorous nutritional standards.

One primary problem with nutritional science has been the focus on 'what's missing'. Early nutritional studies discovered that changes in diet could prevent or cure many ailments. The causes of these ailments were usually the absence of a specific nutrient.

Diseases such as beriberi, scurvy and rickets were found to be caused by nutritional deficiency. These successes influenced the continued search for the missing elements in diet even when that wasn't the problem. It was a search for the 'silver bullet'. This has been a serious problem in more recent decades, since the most prevalent modern health problems are caused by excessive consumption rather than deficiency.

We are slowly losing the vision of the body as a machine found in the textbooks of my childhood. Part of our new vision is understanding the ecology of our own body. We are beginning to understand the immense importance of the relationship between the external environment and the internal one.

Every meal is nourishment for the internal environment of the gut biome. This comprises tens of trillions of individual microorganisms and over 1,000 different species. These colonies of bacteria, viruses and fungi not only have a profound effect on the health of the immune system, metabolism and a variety of body functions, they also affect the functions of the brain.

Gut bacteria produce a wide range of neurochemicals that are used by the brain for memory, learning and mood. Up to 95% of the body's supply of serotonin, a neurotransmitter that contributes to feelings of well-being, is produced in the gut. Serotonin is the feel-good chemical, and it lives in our digestive system. The control factor of all the activity in the microbiome is the food we eat.

Many of the most serious errors in nutrition have resulted from the role of the food industry. Commercial interests make donations to research and universities to influence studies. Many of the studies supporting the health benefits of their commercially produced foods are paid for by the manufacturers, and promote outmoded mythologies regarding food values. This is true of the sugar, beef, poultry and dairy industries, who are often more dominant than nutritionists in the creation of government health guidelines.

Environment

Food is our essential link to the physical world. The quality of food reflects the health of our soil, water and atmosphere. As we alter the environment, we alter our food. We all have to do our best to consider the biological value of how foods are grown and processed, and how they contribute to positive or negative environmental effects.

It is a well-established fact that the single most important contribution that individuals can make to slow the progress of climate change is to stop eating animal products.

Consider: Over 60 billion land animals are killed each year for human consumption. Most estimates are that over a trillion fish are killed each year; the oceans are quickly becoming bereft of life.

Consider: These animals need to be fed, which means cutting down rainforests to grow food for them. They produce faeces and other waste products that find their way into the water table, along with the hormones and antibiotics they are given to ward off sickness and make them grow faster.

Consider: Growing GM foods and following modern agricultural practices means an increase of chemicals that destroy the life of the soil. These methods create erosion and toxic streams, contributing to 'dead zones' when they reach the sea. Damage to the environment creates both direct and indirect health problems for society. It is cause and effect.

The negative environmental impact of the food industry is second to none, and includes:

- Damage and destruction to rainforests through land clearing for animal feed production
- The deterioration of the oceans and the extinction of sea life
- Long-distance transport of animal feed, processed meat and dairy products
- Excessive use of water resources for both feed crops and animal growth
- Toxic run-off of animal waste, often polluted with growth hormones
- Methane gas from cattle.

Economy

The energy that powers human life is food. Proper access to food supplies on a regional basis must be the goal of any global response to the issues of poor nutrition and the wasteful use of resources. Right now, large corporations that grow, process and distribute foods to be shipped long distances consume the land resources of the planet.

Often, foods grown in emerging economies are exotic fruits, beans and nuts. They are grown specifically for export to wealthy countries, and have little nutritional value. In emerging economies this often means that local food production for local consumption disappears. Food needs to be imported, driving prices high and undermining regional self-sufficiency.

The impact of improper use of food resources is often dependent on direct or indirect subsidies that artificially depress the costs of the most harmful agricultural products, meaning that the poor can only afford inadequate nutrition. The cost of this situation in human life and on national economies is steadily rising, along with the cost of treating increasing incidences of heart disease, diabetes and cancer. This pattern will continue unless action is taken.

Social Justice

Many foods that are commonly used are made available only on the backs of social injustice. Slavery is alive and well in the world. Our priorities are:

- Focusing on locally grown perishable foods, such as organically grown fruits and vegetables
- Attempting to use semi-perishable foods, such as organic grains and beans, that are grown as locally as possible
- Using exotic fruits, nuts and condiments as little as possible
- Avoiding processed foods except when the processing has been minimal, and no additives are used
- Researching sources and knowing where your food comes from
- Always supporting the smaller producers.

We try to use only products that are fair trade and organic. This is not a complete solution, but is helpful in creating a food chain with less exploitation. Big agribusiness, fishing and slaughterhouses are where the working conditions are the worst – don't support these industries.

Often the urban poor are trapped in 'food deserts' with little or no access to fresh fruits and vegetables. This is a natural outcome of the modern food industry, and is producing epidemic rates of diabetes and other food-related diseases.

Generally speaking, tropical fruits, nuts and vegetables are likely to be the most exploitative. Check sources and use marginally.

Regard for All Life

We share the world with thousands of species of animals. All of these creatures are essential to the web of life called the biosphere. Most of these animals are sentient: they feel joy, they feel pain, they care for their young and they desire to live. It is time for us to respect their lives and stop killing them for food. If we are immune and insensitive to this mass killing, we should at least know that the killing of these animals produces disease in us and destroys the planet that is the source of our being. Our continuation of killing can only be justified by appealing to sensory pleasure – a sad commentary on our collective humanity.

We struggle in vain to construct a rationale for our actions. We cite science, culture and even God as dictating our use and abuse of our fellow beings, but these attempts all fall short of convincing because of one central issue. Animals are sentient, and our mistreatment of them is unjust, immoral and unnecessary.

What We Eat

Organic, Seasonal and Local when Possible

There are no 'superfoods', only foods that have specific qualities. Most of the foods that form a healthy diet are not particularly loaded with any one nutrient. Healthy foods usually contain a broad range of nutrients and are easy to digest. It is the cooking that brings out the delicious qualities of the food and assist the digestive process.

The food groups listed below are readily available in almost every part of the world. The classifications I am using are not exclusively botanical, but rather based on the groupings that will be familiar to a person shopping in a local market.

Whole Grains

Our Human Ecology Diet has cereal grain as its foundation. Taken as a group, the grains can feed more people per acre with semi-perishable food than any other food. The nourishing qualities of grains, plus the ability to store them for long periods of time with little spoilage, have made them the single most important crop in human history. They have assured societies the capacity to survive through periods of drought or presence of harmful pests. They were insurance against the bad times.

The nutritional profile of grains is excellent. They contain protein, vitamins, minerals, carbohydrate, fats and fibre in forms that are easy to digest and metabolise. Grains are versatile in use and can be made into porridge, breads or noodles.

In North and South America, the primary grains were **maize** (**sweetcorn**), and **quinoa** in the high Andes. **Oats** were primary in the British Isles; **buckwheat** and **barley** in Europe; **wheat**, **millet** and **rice** in the Near and Far East; and **wheat** and **millet** in Africa. These grains became synonymous with settled culture.

When we talk about whole grains we are always referring to unrefined cereal grains. This means that only the inedible husk has been removed. The outside shell of the grain, the cellulose, has not been broken. The grain with this outer skin intact is capable of being sprouted and contains the germ, the carbohydrate and the bran. The micronutrients in the grain are protected. When the outside cellulose is removed the process of oxidation occurs, and the grains begin to lose their nutritional value. This process is what we call 'refining'.

Much of the confusion regarding wholegrain consumption is purposely generated by those who support a high consumption of animal-sourced foods. I consider most of this propaganda to be misleading at best, and completely counterintuitive. Books like *Wheat Belly* and *Grain Brain* are poorly disguised advertisements for the Atkins Diet, and its many more recent incarnations such as the Paleo Diet. These low-carbohydrate diets can produce short-term weight loss but are actually dangerous and unhealthy as a way of eating.

The unsaid truth is that these diets work by reducing *refined* and not wholegrain products, usually containing high-fructose sweeteners and sugar. The contention that grain is responsible for weight gain is proven false when you compare the bodies of those who live on a grain-based diet with those who live on the modern diet of empty calories, high fat and protein. It has only been since the introduction of fast foods that people in traditionally grain-based cultures have suffered from obesity.

Of the three macronutrients (carbohydrates, protein and fat) carbohydrates are needed in the largest amounts. Here are the top reasons complex carbohydrates have such superstar status:

- They are the main source of fuel for your body.
- They are burned most efficiently as a fuel source.
- They are required by your central nervous system (your brain runs almost entirely on glucose and can't use fat or protein for its energy needs), muscles (including your heart) and kidneys.
- They provide glucose to all of your body's cells and tissues for energy.
- They can be stored in your liver and muscles for future energy needs.
- They can be found in whole grains, grain products, beans, vegetables, sea vegetables, fruits, nuts and seeds.

It is refined-flour products that cause the problems. We need to question the saying, 'best thing since sliced bread'. These are products that have virtually no nutritional content, and are usually filled with sugars, fats and chemical agents. The commercial breads (including most 'wholewheat' varieties), biscuits, muffins, cakes and pizza crusts are a nutritional nightmare mix of trans fats, refined grains and simple sugars. These foods raise blood sugar and are difficult to digest.

Rice

Rice has been cultivated in the Far East for 9–10,000 years, and slowly spread into the Near East and into Europe. Mediterranean-style cooking has incorporated rice for centuries, with dishes like paella, stews and risottos.

This is the most nourishing grain and possibly the most delicious. It combines well with almost every vegetable or bean. Its naturally sweet taste can be enjoyed on a daily basis. For a complete meal, eat rice with a bean dish, a variety of vegetables and fermented pickles.

Millet

Millet has been cultivated in the Far East for at least 10,000 years, and eventually spread into Africa where it is used still to this day. In some cultures, it is the principle food crop. In Europe, it was never as popular, but as people have become more used to using whole grains in their diet it has become more popular. Millet is gluten-free and non-allergenic. A great grain for sensitive individuals, and its high protein content (15%) makes it a substantial addition to a vegan diet.

Some may find that lightly roasting millet before using it brings out its sweetness. Often, people use gravies or sauces on top of the millet as it can have a tendency to be a little dry. It can also be used as a porridge, and is good added into soups and stews.

Barley

Barley is a grain that has wonderful warming qualities when eaten but is usually associated with brewing and making beer. It's a wonderful food in the colder months. One of the most popular uses for it is, of course, in soups and stews, as it makes these dishes creamy and hearty. There is nothing nicer on a winter's day than a barley vegetable stew.

Oats

Oats are similar to barley in use; rolled oats and oatmeal are the common forms but the whole grain can be used as porridge. Similar to barley, this is an excellent winter grain, particularly in cold and wet climates. This is because it has more fats than other grains. Steel-cut oats (in the US), also called pinhead oats or coarse oatmeal (in the UK) or Irish oatmeal, are groats (the inner kernel with the inedible hull removed) of whole oats which have been chopped into two or three pieces. Steel-cut oats are traditionally used to make porridge, as well as oat cakes, etc.

Quinoa

Quinoa is often touted as a superfood, particularly because of its high protein content; although, interestingly, oats have more protein than quinoa. This is a grain that thrives in a dry, high environment such as the Andes, where it originates. It is still the principle food for many of the native people that live in those high mountain areas. It has been domesticated for over 7,000 years. Quinoa should be rinsed well before cooking to remove the outer coating, saponin, that can give the grain a slightly bitter taste.

Maize

Maize (**sweetcorn**) is a grain which developed in Meso-America in prehistoric times. Up to the first European landings, most Native American people on the East Coast of America and in the South-West, Mexico and South America were living on a diet that was based around the consumption of maize. Maize can either be eaten fresh as sweetcorn or ground into a meal.

Buckwheat

Buckwheat has a very strong taste; however, some people, me included, love the hearty, earthy taste. Buckwheat is the most warming of all the grains. Its use has been traced back to very cold areas, particularly Mongolia, Tibet, Russia and Finland. It is reported to have been grown since about 5,000 years BC, and in the Balkans was cultivated regularly from about 4,000 BC. Buckwheat is actually a 'pseudo cereal'. It is gluten-free, making it a popular substitute for other wheat-based foods. You can use it as a grain in soups or in sauces, but most people are familiar with it as used in noodles or as a flour product. In whole form, it is eaten primarily as 'Kasha', in noodle form such as soba or as a porridge.

Wheat

Wheat is the most widely used of all the cereal grains. Most of it is ground and made into flour products. Hard wheat varieties have more gluten in them and are therefore used more popularly to make both noodles and flat breads. Wheat products are popular in almost every cuisine around the world in one form or another, usually in breads.

Most problems that are experienced with wheat may be down to three factors:

1. Flour products can cause havoc if there is poor digestion, The whole grain that has not been finely ground is easier to digest. Because the bread dissolves quickly in the mouth, it is seldom chewed well and mixed with the digestive enzymes in the mouth that aid digestion.
2. Breads often contain yeast, sugars, milk or other products that inhibit digestion or create nutritional problems.
3. The presence of excessive gluten. Modern bread and baked-food production has favoured very high gluten varieties of wheat. Making sourdough bread, where commercial yeast is not used, is better if you have no specific problems with bread use.

The sourdough process uses a starter that contains naturally occurring lactobacilli and yeasts. The fermentation that takes place makes the bread more digestible, and it needs less gluten (can be made with low-gluten varieties of grain) and does not create the lift in blood glucose that yeasted bread does.

Our **Human Ecology Diet** recommends at least two servings a day of whole grains. One of these servings should be unrefined whole grain and the other naturally fermented breads or noodles.

Beans

Beans are usually mentioned in relation to protein for those consuming a plant-based diet. The concept of 'first-class' or 'complete' protein dies hard. The focus on meat protein as being superior deflects the issue away from the simple fact that all plants contain protein. It would be more accurate to call animal protein 'second-hand' protein.

Most plants and microorganisms can synthesise all 20 of the standard amino acids that are needed for life. Animals, including humans, are unable to synthesise all of the amino acids, and so must obtain some of them from their diet. Any amino acids that are needed and cannot be synthesised are referred to as 'essential' amino acids. Humans need to obtain 8 amino acids exclusively from the food they eat.

Some plants contain all the essential amino acids; these include quinoa, buckwheat, soybeans, chia seeds and hemp seeds. Combinations of some foods can produce the full range. Rice and beans make one of the most popular combinations, used in one form or another in many cultures.

The key is to consume a variety of plant foods and include both whole grains and beans on a regular basis. This is because while all plant foods contain some of the essential amino acids it is only a few that contain all. Dietary diversity allows the body obtain all the essential amino acids to construct protein as it is needed. That is why grains and beans are part of the foundation of the Human Ecology Diet.

Cooking beans

A word about cooking beans is worth a few moments. Some people seem to have a rough time with them. Beans are available dried or in jars or cans (we would suggest avoiding all foods in cans that are made from aluminium). Not only are dried beans less expensive than precooked beans, they are also measurably more delicious after they're cooked at home. The rule of thumb is that one cup of dried beans yields three cups of cooked beans.

Cooking in a pressure cooker (or a slow cooker, crockpot, etc.) is basically the same as the stove-top process, but with a few minor changes, stated below. Start with exactly the same steps. Sort and wash the beans, then cover them with filtered water and let them soak overnight with a piece of kombu seaweed. Whether you use a pressure cooker or crockpot, follow these instructions for deliciously cooked beans every time. Soaking beans shortens their cooking time and makes them more digestible.

Pressure cookers cook beans very quickly compared with ordinary stove-top cooking. Most recipes call for anywhere between 30 and 45 minutes of cooking time, but different varieties of beans may require an adjustment. Beans taste great (some may say better) after a day or two, so don't worry about spoilage. Leftovers can be reused in soups or stews.

Black (turtle) beans

Black (turtle) beans are a small, shiny variety of the common bean especially popular in Latin American cuisine, though can also be found in the Cajun and Creole cuisines of southern Louisiana. Like most common beans, they are native to the Americas, but have been introduced around the world.

Kidney beans

Kidney beans are a major source of protein, and provide all the essential amino acids. Studies have revealed that the darker the colour of the skin of the beans, the higher their antioxidant content. They are also high in fibre, magnesium, iron and copper.

Adzuki beans

Adzuki beans are small, compact, shiny red beans that are lower in fat and oil than other beans. Adzuki beans are easier to digest than most beans, and in Asia are thought to strengthen the kidneys.

Chickpeas

Chickpeas (**garbanzo beans**) have a wonderful nutty taste and creamy texture when cooked. They are wonderful to use in bean dishes, combined with sweet vegetables or sweetcorn, as well as in soups and stews. The choline in chickpeas helps with sleep, muscle movement, learning and memory.

Pinto beans

Pinto beans are a very good source of cholesterol-lowering fibre, as are most other beans. In addition to lowering cholesterol, pinto beans' high fibre content prevents blood sugar levels from rising too rapidly after a meal, making these beans an especially good choice for individuals with diabetes, insulin resistance or hypoglycaemia. When combined with whole grains such as brown rice, pinto beans provide virtually fat-free, high quality protein.

Lentils

Lentils are an ancient legume and come in many varieties, from common brown-green and red to yellow and puy lentils (a tiny, sweet French variety, which is great in salads). Very high in protein and minerals and with a full-bodied, peppery taste, lentils are good in everything from stews and soups to salads and side dishes. Low in calories and high in nutrition, lentils are the perfect legume to eat in the summer in salads and make delicious soups and stews for the colder months of winter.

Soybeans and soy products

Soy beans are always mentioned as the most efficient way to achieve the full complement of amino acids. In the Far East, they have proved a life-saving crop for many centuries. There is a huge difference between the ways that soy foods have been traditionally used in Asia compared with their more recent use in the West.

Using the Western approach to nutritional science, the soybean was recognised as a valuable source of protein but not really studied in terms of its normal dietary use. This has stimulated a commercial rush to put soy into anything and call it a 'health food'. Soy is now found in a variety of products such as soy milk, soy yogurt and imitation meat products, and as a filler in many standard grocery items. It is also a popular source of feed for animals.

Vegetarian diets and other plant-based approaches to nutrition were common in Asia, and people developed simple food technologies to create healthy foods from vegetable sources. The benefits of the soybean were prized, but understood to be present only when the beans were processed, mostly through fermentation. Foods like **miso paste**, **tempeh**, **soy sauce** and a wide variety of soy foods were developed. These foods are unique and very valuable. The process of fermentation makes the nutrients more bioavailable. It is important to note that these foods are used in relatively small amounts in the daily diet. Without fermentation, soy is more difficult to digest. This is especially true with children, and soy milk should not be given to infants as a formula to replace mother's milk.

Miso is a traditional Japanese seasoning produced by fermenting soybeans with koji (a fungus), and has long been suspected to be one of the most significant reasons behind the high levels of health among the Japanese. Miso is a probiotic, containing living microorganisms. Miso's lactic acid bacteria help to maintain a healthy digestive system. The fermentation by the fungi creates an environment in which the probiotic bacteria (the 'good bacteria' that your gut requires) thrive. These bacteria include lactobacilli, which have been shown to increase the availability, quantity, digestibility and absorption of nutrients in the body.

Soy protein isolate is a favourite ingredient in artificial soy meat substitutes. Soy burgers, soy sausages and lunch meats are mostly touted as healthy replacements for meat. The problem is that the products are made from soybeans (usually GM) that have had all the fat removed and been washed in a chemical bath or water to remove the natural sugars and fibre. Soy protein isolate is a highly processed ingredient and is best avoided.

Tempeh is a good example of a natural protein-rich food. It is made by using a controlled fermentation process that binds hulled, cooked soybeans into a cake form. Tempeh originated in Indonesia and is still a staple there. The beans are mixed with a mould spore starter and incubated for two days. As a result of the process, the soy protein in tempeh becomes more digestible. Tempeh is fibre-rich and a healthy source of vegetable protein, minerals and soy isoflavones.

Tempeh is always cooked before eating; you can steam, boil, bake or sauté it. You can enjoy it with a wide variety of grains, vegetables or noodles, or use it in soups, salads and sandwiches. It is very versatile addition to a healthy diet.

Tofu has been a staple food throughout Asia for the past 2,000 years. Tofu is known for its good nutritional and culinary versatility. It has a cheese-like quality and is laboriously made by curdling 'milk' made from boiled soybeans with a natural coagulant. Tofu blends with and absorbs flavours from other foods. Rich in B vitamins and a vegetable protein source, tofu is often portrayed as a meat substitute. Tofu is taken traditionally with miso soup as a meal, but it's perfectly fine to use in the occasional dessert, marinated burgers or sauces, and savoury creams. Always buy a brand that is made from organic whole soy beans. Tofu is an excellent protein as it has all the 8 essential amino acids. When using these soy foods, it is always good to read the labels and use only products that are certified organic and made with non-GM beans.

Our **Human Ecology Diet** recommends daily consumption of one cup of beans or bean products in soups, stews or salads.

Vegetables

Vegetables reflect the changing of the seasons; the different colours that they show indicate the phytonutrients that are in the foods. A good guideline is to always try to eat any perishable food from local sources and in the season of its growth. Be particular about organic quality. The challenge is to consider these things but to make sure to get variety. This is particularly true if you live in an area where local weather, poor soil or lack of local variety is a problem. There are hundreds of varieties of vegetables. Listed below are general characteristics of some popular ones.

Cruciferous vegetables

Cruciferous vegetables are very important for most people living in the northern hemisphere in a four-season climate. They include cabbage, broccoli, cauliflower and curly kale. Vegetables in this particular family are best when they are cooked. They can sometimes be a little bit difficult to digest if they are not cooked well. Cabbage has been a staple food in Europe for centuries, both cooked and fermented as sauerkraut.

These vegetables are very nutrient dense, and they are often known to have particular healing modalities, including anti-inflammatory properties.

Cruciferous vegetables include: **arugula**, **pak choi (bok choi)**, **broccoli**, **broccoli rabe**, **Brussels sprout**, **cabbage**, **cauliflower**, **Chinese cabbage**, **collard greens**, **daikon**, **kale**, **kohlrabi**, **radish**, **swede (rutabaga)** and **turnip**.

Squashes

Squashes are a very diverse family of vegetables that originate in the northern hemisphere in the Americas; the cultivation of food crops in both North and South America has rotated around maize (sweetcorn), beans and squash. They were sometimes referred to as the 'three sisters'. The combination of these three foods gave people an incredibly rich and nutritionally diverse diet which sustained native peoples of North America for centuries before the arrival of Europeans.

They are a fantastic autumn and winter food. They can be stored for months without losing their nutritional value. They are a great source of complex carbohydrates and are very sweet to the taste, so they are very useful in cooking. Their sweetness makes them popular as both vegetable dishes, often cooked with beans, and in desserts.

The squash family includes: **pumpkin**, **acorn squash**, **Hokkaido pumpkin**, **butternut squash**, **cheese pumpkin**, **Hubbard squash**, **kabocha squash** and **turban squash**.

Roots and tubers

These are vegetables that grow below the ground, and most of the roots and tubers have been used traditionally all over the world as good sources of complex carbohydrate. They have often been used as a primary food source when climate or other environmental conditions were not favourable to growing grains. Some tubers have an even broader range of nutrients than grains. This is probably why before grain cultivation and in semi-tropical climates they were the principle foods.

Roots are the energy storage system of the plant. Similar to some of the other foods that we have talked about, these foods are nutritionally dense and have traditionally been considered as essentials to a healthy diet. Foods like carrots and onions, potatoes, yams and sweet potatoes will last a long time without losing their nutritional qualities.

These vegetables include: (some listed earlier as cruciferous as well) **carrots**, **daikon**, **parsley root**, **parsnips**, **beetroot**, **celeriac**, **radish**, **swede** (**rutabaga**), **turnip**, **burdock**, **salsify**, **taro**, and the most popular tuberous roots – **sweet potato**, **yams** and **potato**. **Onion**, **garlic**, **shallots**, **spring onion** and **leeks** are also roots, though botanically they are alliums.

Hearty greens

Hearty greens are a basic requirement for healthy eating. Some cruciferous vegetables mentioned earlier will fit into this category. If you are eating a plant-based diet, I think it is very important to have green vegetables every day. The unique concentration of nutrients in dark green vegetables lies in the rich mix of vitamins and minerals. These greens pack a more significant punch than the salad greens we will talk about next. If you have a good seasonal balance, you are going to have a good nutritional balance.

The dark green vegetables include, but are not limited to: **collards**, **mustard greens**, **turnip greens**, **chard**, **spinach** and **kale**. Most of these vegetables are best lightly cooked (more so with kale).

Lighter greens (salad vegetables)

Even when the climate is cold, people (especially those who have eaten a lot of animal fats) need some raw food. Raw foods are helpful in cleaning out the gut and dissolving fatty tissue. Have small amounts of raw food daily – but remember it's easy to eat too much of it in a cooler climate.

Whether it's pressed salads or light fresh salads, they are best used more in the warm months and slightly less in the cooler months. Varieties of lettuce, rocket, or any of the spring greens can be eaten raw and are good to have on a daily basis.

These salad vegetables are relaxing by nature. Aside from their cooling qualities, they are an excellent source of vitamins – and of enzymes. We manufacture enzymes in our bodies, but it's good to get some in our diet (although many are destroyed during digestion). Eating salad vegetables or raw vegetables ensures that you get the full spectrum of foods you need.

Vegetables reflect the seasons, so let the seasons be your guide. Food is often shipped long distances, so use produce that has travelled only when local or regional supplies are inadequate.

Vegetables that are seldom cooked include: **arugula**, **endive**, **chicory**, **dandelion greens**, **escarole**, **radicchio**, **watercress**, **iceberg lettuce**, **bibb lettuce** and **romaine lettuce**.

Fermented vegetables

Fermented vegetables are important probiotics; good to have in small portions daily. **Sauerkraut**, one of the most common, is easy to make. Making fresh fermented foods can really promote a healthy gut biome. There are good quality commercial sauerkrauts on the market, but making it at home is a satisfying project.

Juicing and sprouting

Juicing and sprouting are quite popular now, particularly in warmer seasons and climates. Many advocates of juicing and sprouting live in warmer areas such as Florida or Southern California, where refreshing foods make sense.

Sprouting is a good way of having salads and that light freshness in your diet all year round. Sprouting seeds or beans is, simply, germinating them. You rinse the seeds or beans to clean them, and then soak them for up to 12 hours (depending on the type of seed). You drain them, and rinse at regular intervals. As they germinate, the nutrients are broken down and become more available.

Sprouts can be used all year round and are used daily in my kitchen. **Mung beans**, **alfalfa**, **broccoli seeds** and **lentils** are all easy to sprout. Add them to just about anything, from soups to salads and grain dishes.

Juicing has become more popular as chewing has become less popular. When you juice, notice the amount of pulp that is left behind. That pulp is part of the nutrient base of the food. Removing it challenges our digestion, and wastes valuable minerals, fibre and vitamins. Ecologically, economically and from a health point of view it is a wasteful process.

The nightshade vegetables

These vegetables are permeated with mythology. As a reflection of our macrobiotic influence we should mention this family of vegetables. Nightshades include plants with some toxic features (such as tobacco and belladonna). Common food plants such as **potatoes** and **tomatoes**, **aubergine** (**eggplant**) and **peppers** are part of this family.

There are chemical compounds that have a tendency to exacerbate inflammation within these plants. They are used sparingly in modern macrobiotic cooking and always cooked. The cooking reduces the solanine, one of the offending substances. You will notice that I have used tomato in some recipes, but always cooked well.

Sea vegetables

Sea vegetables have been used as a food in many parts of the world, usually as a condiment or cooked with other foods. They were traditionally consumed regularly, in moderate amounts. We normally associate their use with Japan and Korea, but they were also part of the traditional Welsh, Scottish and Irish diets.

Many sea vegetables help in the pre-digestion of pulses, which reduces the production of gas. They are low in fat; very low in calories; and rich in essential minerals, vitamins and protein. They have high levels of calcium, iron and iodine, as well as vitamins A, B, C and E. All sea vegetables contain significant amounts of protein, sometimes as much as 48%.

The sea vegetables include: **nori**, **kombu**, **arame**, **hijiki** and **dulse**.

It is important to check with distributors that all sea vegetables have been harvested from clean waters and have been tested for heavy metals. This is the same as demanding organic growing for vegetables. There are many good sources – do your homework.

Our **Human Ecology Diet** recommends cooked vegetables at every meal: mixed salad leaves including sprouts (depending on climate) and a small portion of fermented vegetables daily; sea vegetables in miso broth or used as a condiment once a day. It's a good idea to have both root vegetables and leafy greens.

Fruit

'Eat more fruit and vegetables' is a familiar 'health' message that blurs good nutritional lines in several ways. Fruit is high in sugar. This sugar (fructose) is not as disruptive to the system as the refined fructose we discussed earlier. This is particularly true when consumed in a whole fruit, but it is still a simple form of sugar that is absorbed into the system quickly. The fibre, minerals and vitamins found in the whole fruit buffer the impact of the sugars on the system.

Sugar comes in several different forms, including glucose, fructose and sucrose. Glucose is the healthiest source of energy. Carbohydrates such as those in grains and vegetables break down into glucose, your body's main source of fuel. Fructose is the only type of sugar found in fruits. When eaten in excess, it presents health challenges similar to those of the simpler refined sugars. Given the huge difference in sugar content from fruit to fruit, it's almost impossible to suggest how much to consume.

People who cut back on all simple sugars for a month or two commonly become more sensitive to more complex forms of sugar in their food. Until then, people really do not perceive the sweetness in a carrot or in brown rice, partly because you have to chew in order for the carbohydrates to begin breaking down into sugars. The more we consume simpler forms of sugar (like fructose), the less we detect the sugars in other foods. So, we need to re-educate our taste buds.

Fruits are, in general, very perishable. So, they are best eaten fresh, and in season (and local, where possible). Tropical fruits are the highest in sugars and acid; fruits grown further from the equator have less sugar. Drinking the juice of fruits is probably the worst form of consumption, since the sugars are more concentrated, and the buffering agents have been removed. Sugars are also concentrated in dried fruit, so a raisin has a higher sugar content than a grape.

Eating fruit in smaller amounts is generally a good idea. Fruit can also be cooked into purees and sauces, or baked. It makes great fillings for pies or as a smooth dessert dish. Think of fruit as a pleasure food, not an essential. There is nothing you can get from fruit that you cannot get from vegetables. It is a good idea to have fruit an hour or so after a meal, or between meals, for best digestion. some non-tropical fruits are: **apples**, **strawberries**, **cherries**, **blueberries**, **watermelons**, **cantaloupes**, **peaches**, **plums**, **raspberries**, **pears** and **apricots**.

Our **Human Ecology Diet** recommends fresh seasonal fruit once or twice a day. Frozen fruits are also excellent for using in desserts.

Nuts and Seeds

Seeds and nuts are an excellent source of protein and fat. When left in their shells, they are easy to store for a long time. They may be used as condiments with grains or vegetable dishes or roasted as a snack. Roasting nuts and seeds releases their oils, making them easier to digest. But all nuts are not created equal.

Allergic reactions to nuts principally affect young children, and may be severe, even life-threatening. A smaller number of people have allergic responses to seeds. Possible symptoms of these allergies are hives or swelling, trouble breathing, tightness of the throat, nausea, abdominal pain and diarrhoea.

Less than 1% of the population has a peanut allergy. The symptoms can vary from mild to severe. Generally, those with allergies are allergic to several foods, the most common being milk, eggs, shellfish and wheat. Between 1997 and 2008 the number of children reported with nut allergies more than tripled. This has run parallel to an increase in cases of asthma and eczema.

The **tree nuts**, such as **macadamias**, **cashews**, **brazil nuts**, **hazelnuts**, **pecans** and **walnuts** all have a high fat content. The walnut and hazelnut are native to Europe. All tree nuts originate in sub-tropical climates, except pecans – the only native North American tree nut.

Chestnuts are used in many parts of the northern hemisphere, and have the least fat of any nut; they are rich in carbohydrates and the only nut that contains vitamin C. **Peanuts** have among the highest amounts of oil in this group. They are from a different botanical family than true tree nuts, but are commonly thought of as a nut. A handful of any of the tree nuts supplies more than the daily requirement of healthy fats.

Seeds are often used as a garnish on foods, particularly with wholegrain dishes. We use seeds daily on grain dishes. **Pumpkins seeds**, **sesame seeds**, **sunflower seeds**, **chia seeds**, **flax seeds** and **hemp seeds** are all sources of omega oils and add flavour and variety to the diet.

Our **Human Ecology Diet** recommends roasted seeds or nuts daily as a garnish, or taken as a snack if you are not overweight.

A Japanese miscellany

Most of the foods in my recipes can be purchased in a supermarket. The most important basic foods are grains, beans, vegetables, fruits, nuts and seeds. These foods will make up about 95% of what you eat, or more. The rest of your diet will be cooking condiments and speciality foods. These foods enhance the health benefits of your diet and create a broader range of diversity.

Some of these foods come from the Japanese tradition that lies at the foundation of the macrobiotic diet, and some come from dietary traditions in other parts of the world. The importance of these foods is that they were developed in the Far East by cultures that focused on a plant-based approach to eating. There may be some ingredients that you are unfamiliar with. This list will give you a general guideline on their usage.

Agar-agar

Agar-agar is made from seaweed and used as a gelling agent in place of gelatine in jellies. Its mild flavour and total lack of calories have made it a favourite with health-conscious and vegan cooks around the world. Even at room temperature, it sets quickly as it cools, and seals in the natural flavour and sweetness of any fruits and vegetables used with it, as well as having the benefit of a naturally high fibre content. Often used as a thickening agent.

Adzuki beans

Adzuki beans are small and very compact, with a deep reddish-brown colour. These tiny beans are a staple in the Far East. They are revered in Japan for their healing properties and are low in fat and more digestible than most other beans, as well as being a rich source of potassium and iron and B vitamins (but not B12).

Arame

A large leafy sea vegetable, arame is finely shredded and boiled before drying and packed for selling. Since it is precooked, it requires far less cooking time than other sea vegetables and can be marinated for salads with no cooking at all. One of the milder tasting sea plants, it is a great source of protein and minerals, calcium and potassium.

Bancha tea (kukicha)

This Japanese tea made from the stems and twigs of the tea bush has no caffeine or chemical dyes and is packed with antioxidants. It is high in calcium and aids digestion owing to its alkalising effect (it lowers acidity). This tea also burns fat and lowers cholesterol.

Ginger

Ginger is used liberally in Chinese cooking and in many Asian countries. A golden-coloured, spicy root vegetable with a variety of uses in cooking, it imparts a mild, peppery taste to cooking and is commonly used in stir-fries, sautés, sauces and dressings. Shaped like fingers of a hand, ginger has the reputation of stimulating circulation with its hot taste. A very popular remedy in Oriental medicine for helping with everything from joint pain to stomach aches and acid indigestion.

Hokkaido pumpkin

There are two varieties of Hokkaido pumpkin. One has a deep orange colour and the other has a light green skin, similar to Hubbard squash. Both varieties are very sweet and have a tough outer skin.

Kombu

A sea vegetable packaged in wide, dark, dehydrated strips that will double in size when soaked and cooked. Kombu is a great source of glutamic acid, a natural flavour enhancer. Adding a small piece to soups and stews deepens flavours. It is also generally believed that kombu improves the digestibility of grains and beans when added to these foods in small amounts.

Kuzu

Kuzu is a high quality starch made from the root of the kuzu plant, native to the mountains of Japan and different to the weed 'kudzu' found in America. Kuzu grows like a vine, with tough roots. It is used primarily as a thickener and in medicinal teas. It is reputed to strengthen the digestive tract owing to its alkaline nature.

Maitake mushrooms

Medical researchers have been studying the antitumour activity of mushrooms. They seem to stimulate the immune system's T-cells. Maitakes are considered the king of mushrooms, because they are so delicious and have a reputation as a very powerful healing food. Enjoy them in soups, stews and teas.

Mirin

Mirin is a Japanese rice wine with a sweet taste and very low alcohol content. Made by fermenting sweet brown rice with water and koji (a cultured rice), mirin adds depth and dimension to sauces, glazes and various other dishes.

Miso

Miso is a fermented soy-bean paste used traditionally to flavour soups but prized throughout Asia for its ability to strengthen the digestive system. Traditionally aged miso is a great source of high quality protein. Available in a wide variety of flavours and strengths, the most nutritious miso is made from barley and soy beans and is aged for at least two years. Miso is rich in digestive enzymes, which are delicate and should not be boiled. Just light simmering of miso activates and releases the enzymes' strengthening qualities into food.

Nori (sea laver)

Usually sold in paper-thin sheets, nori is a great source of protein and minerals like calcium and iron. Most well known as a principal ingredient in sushi, nori has a mild, sweet flavour, just slightly reminiscent of the ocean. Great for strengthening grain and noodle dishes, floating in soup or adding to stir-fries.

Pressed salad

Pressed salads are made by very thinly slicing or shredding fresh vegetables, and combining with a pickling agent such as sea salt, umeboshi, brown rice vinegar or tamari soy sauce, and placing in a pickle press. In the pickling process, many of the enzymes and vitamins are retained, while the vegetables become easier to digest.

Rice syrup (brown rice syrup, rice malt)

The Japanese call this 'liquid sweetness'. Rice syrup is a thick, amber syrup made by combining sprouted barley with cooked brown rice and storing it in a warm place. Fermentation begins and the starches in the rice covert to maltose and some other complex sugars, making this syrup a wonderfully healthy sweetener. Complex sugars release slowly into the blood stream, providing fuel for the body, rather than wreaking havoc on the blood sugar. Rice syrup's wonderful delicate sweetness makes it ideal for baked goods and other deserts.

Sea vegetables

The exotic vegetables that are harvested from the sea coast and nearby rocks are high in protein and rich in minerals. Readily available in dehydrated form in natural foods stores, sea vegetables are growing in popularity for their nutritional benefits and ability to enhance the flavours in other foods.

Seitan (wheat gluten)

Often called 'wheat meat', seitan is made from wheat gluten. Made by kneading the bran and starch out of flour, raw seitan is rather bland, so most commercial brands are simmered in savoury vegetable broth before sale. A wonderful source of protein, it is low in calories and fat and is very popular in Asian 'mock meat' dishes, as well as in hearty stews and casseroles.

Sesame tahini

A thick, creamy paste made from ground hulled sesame seeds, it is used for flavouring everything from sauces to salad dressings to dips, spreads and baked goods.

Shiitake mushrooms

These mushrooms are loaded with nutrition and very powerful for lowering cholesterol and triglyceride levels and cleansing blood. Scientists have recently isolated substances from shiitake that may play a role in the cure and prevention of heart disease, cancer and AIDS. Shiitake mushrooms can be found in natural food stores and many supermarkets. They have an intensely earthy taste, so a few go a long way. It is necessary to soak the dried ones until tender, about 20 minutes, before cooking. Use the soaking water. Trim off the stems as they can be bitter tasting. They are wonderful in soups, stews, gravies, sauces and medicinal teas.

Shoyu (soy sauce)

A confusing term because shoyu is the generic term for Japanese soy sauce as well as the term for a specific type of traditionally made soy sauce, the distinguishing characteristic of which is the use of cracked wheat as the fermenting starter, along with soybeans. The best shoyu is aged for at least two years. This is a lighter seasoning than tamari. Shoyu is high in glutamic acid, a natural form of monosodium glutamate (MSG), which makes it an excellent flavour enhancer, great for marinating, pickling and sautéing.

Soba
A noodle made from buckwheat flour. Some varieties contain other ingredients, like wheat flour or yam flour, but the best quality soba is made primarily of buckwheat flour.

Soybeans
Soybeans are the base for many natural food products, from miso to soy sauce to tofu and tempeh to soymilk to soy flour. On their own, soybeans are rather bland and hard to digest, so are more commonly made into other products. However, when cooked on their own, and long and slow cooking is the only way, soybeans are most delicious.

Soy foods
A catch-all term for the wide range of foods that have soybeans as their base, including soy milk, tofu, tempeh, soy sauce, tamari, shoyu, miso, soy cheese, soy oil, etc. Avoid texturised soy protein (TVP or TSP) products, such a soy granules and many imitation meat products. They are highly processed and can cause digestive issues. It is also important to note that soy milk is not a healthy option for infants on a plant-based diet, for the same digestive reasons. If a plant milk is needed, use rice or oat beverage.

Soy sauce
Traditional soy sauce (the same as shoyu) is the product of fermenting soybeans, water, salt and wheat. Containing salt and naturally occurring glutamic acid, soy sauce is a natural flavour enhancer. The finest soy sauces are aged from one to two years, like tamari and shoyu, while commercial soy sauce is synthetically aged in a matter of days, producing a salty, artificially flavoured condiment.

Tamari
A fermented soy sauce product that is actually the liquid that rises to the top of the keg when making miso. This thick, rich flavour enhancer is nowadays produced with a fermentation process similar to that of shoyu, but the starter is wheat-free. Tamari is richer, with a full-bodied taste, and contains more amino acids than regular soy sauce.

Tempeh
Tempeh is a traditional Indonesian soy product created by fermenting split cooked soybeans with a starter. As the tempeh ferments, a white fungal mycelium containing enzymes develops on the surface, making the soybeans more digestible, as well as providing a

healthy range of B vitamins. Tempeh can be used for everything from sandwiches and salads to stews and casseroles.

Tofu (soybean curd)
Tofu is a wonderful source of protein and phytoestrogens and is very versatile. Rich in calcium and cholesterol-free, tofu is made by extracting curd from coagulated soy milk and then pressing it into bricks. Tofu can be used in everything from soups and salads to casseroles, stews and quiches, or as the creamy base to sauces and dressings.

Udon
Flat noodles, much like fettuccine, udon comes in a variety of blends of flours, from all wholewheat to brown rice and lotus root to unbleached white flour. I use the wholewheat variety.

Umeboshi paste
Umeboshi paste is a purée made from umeboshi plums to create a concentrated condiment. Use this sparingly as it is quite salty, but it is a great ingredient in salad dressings and sauces, or spread on corn on the cob.

Umeboshi plums
These are Japanese pickles (actually green apricots) with a fruity, salty taste. Pickled in a salt brine and shiso leaves for at least one year (the longer the better), ume plums are traditionally served as a condiment with various dishes, including grains. Ume plums are reputed to aid in the healing of a wide array of ailments from stomach aches to migraines, because they alkalise the blood.

Umeboshi vinegar (ume su)
This is the salty liquid left over from pickling umeboshi plums. Used as a vinegar, it is great for salad dressings and pickle-making. It is also known as ume plum seasoning.

Vinegar (brown rice)
This is a fermented condiment. While lots of vinegars exist, they can be very acidic, and I use brown rice vinegar made from fermented brown rice and sweet brown rice, umeboshi vinegar (above) and balsamic vinegar. Great for reducing lactic acid in the body.

Wakame
A very delicate member of the kelp family, wakame is most traditionally used in miso soups and salads. It requires only a brief soaking and short cooking time, has a gentle flavour and is a great way to introduce sea vegetables to your diet.

What about Nutrition?

Creating a healthy way of eating is not a science project. It is easy to get distracted by the constant tide of information that tells us about the newest 'superfood' or recently discovered nutritional secret. These revelations are usually simply a way to sell a product. What all the best nutritional science tells us is that creating a healthy diet is really very simple. It involves using the foods that have nourished healthy people for centuries and assuring that we get adequate diversity. I always tell my students and clients that they do not require a diploma in biochemistry to put dinner on the table.

It is seldom the lack of a single nutrient that creates health issues. Poverty is the chief cause of malnutrition. In the developed world, it is excess and not deficiency that creates the most problems. It is our consumption of fat, animal protein and simple sugars that is the major cause of dietary-related disease. The focus on single nutrients usually simply creates fear. Our focus should be on the whole profile of a healthy diet. This does not mean we neglect nutritional science; it simply means that science provides us with a useful checklist to assess our overall food choices.

The nutrients that provide the building blocks for human nutrition are listed below. They contribute most to energy, strength and longer life. As you might expect, the food list includes the foods that reduce digestive stress, provide the best range of both macro and micronutrients, and are most effective in disease prevention. There are five essential nutrients that form the foundation of good nutrition: carbohydrate, protein, fat, vitamins, minerals and water.

Carbohydrate

The body runs on carbohydrate; it is our main source of energy and is especially important for brain function. Glucose is the primary fuel for all the cellular functions of the body.

Carbohydrates can be referred to as starches or sugars. When people hear the words starch or sugar, many run for cover. But the main problem is that in the modern diet most of the carbohydrates are processed and stripped of the nutrients that comprise the whole food. Most criticisms of carbohydrate consumption are dishonest because they make no distinction between the refined and the whole product.

Commercial flour products, noodles, pasta, breakfast cereals, soft drinks, sweets, cakes, muffins, and even diet puddings and desserts are made with refined carbohydrates. These fragmented foods have a propensity to make people put on weight, and can cause trouble by spiking blood sugar, or causing intestinal disorders.

Unrefined carbohydrates are found in whole cereal grains, wholemeal breads and pastas, potatoes, sweet potatoes, beans, most root vegetables, winter squashes and fruit. These are the sources of healthy sugars. They are healthy because they digest slowly and retain the fibre, minerals, vitamins and proteins that slow down the absorption of the sugars and complement their metabolism. In their whole form, they provide a healthy medium for the gut biome.

Recent articles have placed a negative image on lectins. These are carbohydrate-binding proteins present in most plants. They play a role in protecting plants against external pathogens, like fungi, and other organisms. Some common dietary staples, such as cereal grains and legumes, have relatively high concentrations of a variety of lectins. Some authors have proposed adverse health effects of wheat lectin, and discouraged the consumption of foods high in lectins.

The current data about the health effects of dietary lectins, when consumed in cooked, baked or highly processed foods, do not show negative health effects in humans. In fact, they show that consumption of foods containing them reduces the risk of type 2 diabetes, cardiovascular disease and some types of cancer, as well as aiding a more favourable long-term weight management. Cooking transforms food and some scientific research doesn't account for this and so falls short, and is often used to promote new theories of why we should fear foods that have been part of the healthy human diet for centuries.

Common refined sugars are listed on food labels. Sucrose, glucose, dextrose, fructose, maltose and lactose are fundamentally all the same, and should be avoided.

Naturally processed rice or barley malt are the best choices for sweeteners because of their increased mineral and vitamin content. I use maple syrup sometimes for special occasions.

Protein

If carbohydrates are the fuel for the body, proteins are the form. Proteins create the foundation for cells and tissues as well as controlling biochemical reactions and aiding the immune system. Proteins regulate metabolism and hormones, repair damaged cells and create new ones. Proteins are found in all vegetable foods to varying degrees.

A common image is that by eating muscle we gain muscle, because a lot of muscle is constituted from protein. This assumption would be similar to saying that if I read great novels, I am sure to produce a bestseller. All the foods we eat are broken down into their primary elements and then reconstructed according to the specific needs of our body.

When we take in the protein of a cow, a chicken or a pig it has already been made into the cow, chicken or pig. We will have to break it down in order to create a human out of it. Both animal and vegetable proteins need to be broken down.

The basic elements of proteins are amino acids; they are the building blocks we need to create human protein. Out of the 20 amino acids required for good health, 8 are considered essential. These must be present in our diet, but do not need to be in a single food. If you are eating grains, beans and vegetables on a daily basis you are assured of getting all the essential amino acids and, therefore, enough protein.

Beans, for example, are high in the amino acid lysine and low in methionine, while grains have complementary strengths and weaknesses. This means if beans and rice are eaten over the course of a day (or even two days), their amino acids will supplement each other and provide a higher quality protein than either would alone. Traditional cultures have recognised this complementary relationship for thousands of years. The grain and bean combination is near universal in agrarian societies around the world.

Fats

Fats are organic compounds that are only soluble in alcohol (not water). They are also called lipids. They are stored in the body as energy reserves and are important components of cell membranes. In a healthy person they have a protective function in cell structure. This is especially true in terms of epithelial cells. As with carbohydrates and proteins, there is massive confusion about the use of fats in a healthy diet.

Fats are needed to help you absorb vitamins A, D, E and K, the 'fat-soluble vitamins'. Fat also fills your fat cells and insulates your body to help keep you warm. Fats are made of a variety of fatty acids. The need for fatty acids is very small. According to the National Academy of Sciences in the United States, our daily requirement could be achieved by a quarter of a teaspoon of fatty acids a day. Using seeds, nuts, grains and beans, you will easily exceed the minimum requirement.

The main uses of fats traditionally have been for their thermogenic function in cold climates, to produce warmth and insulation and to make food tastier (fats trigger a dopamine response). A high-fat diet is tasty, but challenging to health.

The old good–bad scale had to do with saturated and unsaturated fats. The 'good' fats were generally identified as those unsaturated fats generally found in plant foods. These fats are found in olives, soy, corn, nuts, seeds and, in lesser amounts, in grains and some vegetables. When extracted from their source they remain liquid at room temperature. The usual use for these fats is in the form of vegetable oils. These oils are either chemically processed from the plant or, more rarely, pressed. They are a highly processed product.

For many years, the focus was on reducing the 'bad' saturated animal fats, such as butter, cheese, milk and fatty cuts of meat. So, the food industry began to produce 'low-fat' products and to promote the use of vegetable oils. The trick was to use the 'healthy' vegetable oils and still retain the taste or 'mouth feel' of animal fats. The end result was the same.

Common sense tells us that sticky, fatty foods are difficult to digest and make sticky, fatty blood. It makes no difference if the excess fat is from a vegetable oil or an animal. Vegetable oils have about 120 calories per tablespoon and are 100% fat, with no fibre and almost no nutritional value.

Oil causes our red blood cells to clump together, limiting their ability to absorb and deliver oxygen to our cells. This clumping then leads to a slowing down of our blood flow. Studies have shown that our blood flow decreases by over 30% for the four hours following a fatty meal. You will notice that I do not use added oils in my cooking and yet the food is tasty. Nuts and seeds provide an excellent source of fats in the diet and a clean, nourishing range of tastes.

Vitamins

Vitamins are essential nutrients that we need in small amounts on a regular basis. They are organic chemical compounds that are understood to be either ineffectively produced by the body or that cannot be synthesised. They must be obtained through the diet. There are 13 vitamins needed for good health. There are two primary categories of vitamins, fat-soluble and water-soluble.

Fat-soluble vitamins are stored in fatty tissues of the body and the liver. They are easier to store than water-soluble ones and can stay in the body as reserves for days, some of them for months. They are absorbed through the intestinal lining with the help of fats. Vitamins A, D, E and K are fat-soluble. Vitamins D and K can be made by the body.

Water-soluble vitamins are quickly excreted in urine. Because of this, they do not stay in the body, and they need to be replaced more often than fat-soluble vitamins. Vitamin C and all the B vitamins are water-soluble.

Vitamin A is a fat-soluble vitamin. It is associated with good vision and support for a healthy immune system. It is found in carrots, broccoli, sweet potato, kale, collard greens, apricot, cantaloupe and melon.

Vitamin B1 is a water-soluble vitamin. Deficiencies can cause beriberi. It is found in cereal grains, sunflower seeds, brown rice, wholegrain rye, asparagus, kale, cauliflower, potatoes and oranges.

Vitamin B2 is water-soluble. Deficiency may cause ariboflavinosis, a protein-deficiency disease that can cause dysfunction of the liver. It is usually found in poorer populations. The vitamin is found in asparagus, bananas, persimmons, okra, chard and green beans.

Vitamin B3 is water-soluble. Deficiency may cause pellagra, an illness that causes diarrhoea, mental disturbance and dermatitis. Good sources include avocados, dates, tomatoes, leafy vegetables, broccoli, carrots, sweet potatoes, asparagus, nuts, whole grains, legumes, mushrooms and brewer's yeast.

Vitamin B5 is water-soluble. Deficiency may cause paraesthesia ('pins and needles'). Good sources include whole grains (un-hulled only), broccoli and avocados.

Vitamin B6 is water-soluble. Deficiencies may cause anaemia or peripheral neuropathy (damage to parts of the nervous system other than the brain and spinal cord). Good sources include whole grains, banana, vegetables and nuts.

Vitamin B7 is water-soluble. Deficiency may cause dermatitis or enteritis (inflammation of the intestine). Good sources include nuts, seeds, avocados and sweet potato.

Vitamin B9 is water-soluble. Deficiency during pregnancy is linked to birth defects. Good sources include leafy vegetables, legumes and sunflower seeds. Several fruits and beer contain moderate amounts.

Vitamin B12 is water-soluble. It is the only real concern among essential nutrients for vegans. Deficiency may cause megaloblastic anaemia (a condition where bone marrow produces abnormal and immature red blood cells). B12 Is made by bacteria found in the soil and in the intestines of animals. Although humans produce B12 in the digestive tract, it is not reabsorbed to any significant degree. The vitamin can be stored in the body for a period of up to six years in adults.

B12 is crucial for a healthy nervous system, and a chronic lack can eventually cause neurological symptoms. It is recommended that we consume B12 in foods such as fortified yeast extracts or nutritional yeast. Vegans are advised to take a supplement. In some early macrobiotic teaching, there were claims that some fermented foods such as miso and tempeh contained significant amounts of B12; however, this would only be true if the products were made in an environment where there was a high rate of bacterial 'contamination' not found in modern production. Our obsession with protecting ourselves from harmful bacteria means that we do not profit from the direct or indirect benefits of the helpful ones.

It's easy to see why we might imagine B12 to be in foods that do not, in fact, contain it. There can be B12 analogues that do not function as B12 but resemble it in analyses. Some of them are harmless, but others attach to receptor sites and block them. Home-made tempeh, for example, would quite probably have B12, and so might home-fermented vegetables such as sauerkraut. Uniquely among vegetable-sourced foods, nori seaweed has been shown to have significant amounts of active B12.

Many vegans use fortified breakfast cereals, fortified soy milk and fortified meat analogues to provide themselves with adequate B12. This can certainly solve the nutrition issue; however, I prefer to take a simple supplement and avoid 'fortified' foods. Specific brands of nutritional yeast are a reliable source. Be sure to check the nutritional facts label or the ingredients list to ensure you are receiving the active form of vitamin B12, called cobalamin or cyanocobalamin. It is easy to find vegan B12 supplements on the Internet or in grocery shops in developed countries.

A small number of people with no obvious reliable source of B12 appear to have avoided clinical deficiency for 20 years or more. The issue needs more study, but supplementing is the best clear route. B12 is the only vitamin that is not recognised as being reliably supplied from a varied wholefood, plant-based diet with plenty of fruit and vegetables, together with exposure to sun. Vegans using supplements are less likely to suffer from B12 deficiency than those eating a meat-centred, British diet, with up to one in ten of that population suffering from a deficiency.

Vitamin C is water-soluble. It is a powerful antioxidant that can help prevent cell damage. Deficiency may cause megaloblastic anaemia, related to DNA damage in the creation of red blood cells. Good sources include fruit and vegetables. Cooking destroys vitamin C, and so a small amount of raw vegetables or fruits is a good idea.

Vitamin D is fat-soluble. It aids in the absorption of calcium, for strong bones. Deficiency may cause rickets and osteomalacia (softening of the bones). Vitamin D is produced in the skin after exposure to UV (ultraviolet) light from the sun or artificial sources. It is also found in mushrooms.

Vitamin E is fat-soluble and is an antioxidant. Deficiency is uncommon but may cause haemolytic anaemia in newborns (a condition where blood cells are destroyed and removed from the blood too early). Good sources include almonds, avocados, nuts, leafy green vegetables, wheatgerm and whole grains.

Vitamin K is fat-soluble and is essential for blood clotting. Deficiency may cause bleeding diathesis (an unusual susceptibility to bleeding). Good sources include leafy green vegetables, avocados, kiwi fruit and parsley.

Minerals

The minerals in our diet are important for building strong bones and teeth, blood, skin, hair, and muscle, and for nerve function and metabolic processes. We need quite large quantities of **calcium**, **chloride**, **magnesium**, **phosphorus**, **potassium**, **sodium** and **sulphur**. Other minerals, commonly referred to as 'trace minerals', are essential in tiny amounts. They include **iron**, **nickel**, **zinc**, **iodine**, **selenium**, **silicon**, **chromium**, **molybdenum**, **vanadium**, and **cobalt**. Eating a diverse plant-based diet such as the Human Ecology Diet ensures sufficient consumption of all these elements.

Potassium, **sodium**, **calcium**, **magnesium** and **chloride** are electrolytes that can be found in almost all vegetables. Electrolytes are substances that conduct electrical charges when dissolved in water. They regulate nerve and muscle functions, body pH, blood pressure and the rebuilding of damaged tissue. An imbalance in electrolyte levels can lead to either weak muscles, or muscles that contract too severely.

Calcium and **phosphorus** help support bone health. They are abundantly available in a wide variety of plant-based foods, including kale and collard greens, sweet potatoes, broccoli, carrots, chickpeas and almost every other kind of legume, whole grains, and fruit.

Iron is essential for blood production. About 70% of your body's iron is found in the red blood cells (in the protein haemoglobin) of your blood, and in muscle cells (in the protein myoglobin). Haemoglobin carries oxygen from the lungs to the cells and tissues. Iron is found in green leafy vegetables, beans and dried fruits.

Zinc ensures your immune system functions well. It plays a role in cell division, cell growth, wound healing and the breakdown of carbohydrates. Zinc is also needed for cognition and the senses of smell and taste.

Iodine is needed to make thyroid hormones, which control the body's metabolism and are essential for proper bone and brain development during pregnancy and infancy. Iodine deficiency is a global public health concern, affecting nearly one-third of people worldwide. Because the iodine content varies widely in soil, it's unreliable in plant foods. Sea vegetables can either have a lot of iodine or very little. The best sources are navy beans, potatoes with their skins on and dried sea vegetables. Dulse and kelp are the best sources.

Minerals are found in abundance in all green vegetables, which of course are a part of any healthy diet. All of the 56 minerals essential for human health are present in sea vegetables (including calcium, magnesium, potassium, iodine, iron and zinc) together with important trace elements, such as selenium (often lacking in land vegetables due to soil demineralisation). The minerals in sea vegetables exist in a chelated colloidal form that makes them easier to digest and utilise. Although usually consumed in small amounts, they can be an important part of a healthy diet.

Water

Hydration is a very important aspect of health. By weight, we are 65% water, 20% protein, 12% fats, and a few incidentals on top of that. By number of molecules, we are pretty much entirely water.

We are like luscious plums when we are born but become like dried-up prunes as we age (internally as well as externally). Drinking water is something I am always passionate about teaching to all our students and clients, as most people are constantly dehydrated.

Here is an easy rule of thumb! Drink two glasses when you rise, one to two glasses before lunch, and the same before dinner. Avoid drinking while eating as it dilutes the digestive enzymes. Build up to this if you must, but it is an important part of healing to hydrate at a deep cellular level. Obviously, sip on water throughout the day if required. Please do not drink cold beverages, particularly with ice, as it chills the kidneys. Drink natural spring or filtered water at room temperature. Make sure to use a filtered water system to get the best hydration possible. Bottled water is dead and leaches carbon dioxide from the plastic. Water is important to facilitate discharge of toxins from the body.

As a child, my six siblings and I were brought up on water. No tea, no coffee, just plain old water was the Watson beverage. Even at 93 years old, my mum still drinks her hot water twice a day and has never drunk tea or coffee. Being aware of the importance of hydration and drinking water is something that has been a constant in my daily life.

Resources

Recommended Reading

Listed below are my most trusted sources, which we recommend to all our students for furthering their studies. I have endless appreciation for all of these fine authors, who have dedicated their lives to educating others.

Barnard, Neal. *Dr. Barnard's Programme For Reversing Diabetes*. Pennsylvania: Rodale, 2006.
———. *The Cheese Trap*. USA: Grand Central Life and Style, 2017.
Campbell, T. Colin. *The China Study*. Dallas: Benbella Books, 2005.
———. *Whole*. Dallas: Benbella Books, 2013.
Carson, Rachel. *The Silent Spring*. New York: Penguin, 1962.
Francione, Gary L., and Anna E. Charlton. *Eat Like You Care*. New Jersey: Exempla, 2013.
Kushi, Michio. *The Macrobiotic Way*. New Jersey: Avery Books, 1985.
McDougall, John. *The Healthiest Diet on The Planet*. New York: Harper One, 2016.
———. *The Starch Solution*. Pennsylvania: Rodale, 2012.
Sha, Nandita. *Reversing Diabetes in 21 Days*. India: Penguin Random House, 2017.
Tara, Bill. *Macrobiotics and Human Behaviour*. New York: Japan Publications, 1985.
———. *Natural Body, Natural Mind*. Indiana: Xlibris, 2008.
———. *How To Eat Right & Save The Planet*. New York: Square One Publishing, 2019.
Varona, Verne. *Macrobiotics for Dummies*. Indiana: Wiley, 2009.
Watson-Tara, Marlene. *Macrobiotics for All Seasons*. Chichester: Lotus, 2012.

Website Listings and Resources

Marlene Watson-Tara and Bill Tara	www.macrovegan.org
T. Colin Campbell	www.nutritionstudies.org
Dr John McDougall	www.drmcdougall.com
Professor Gary L. Francione	www.howdoigovegan.com
Dr Michael Klaper	www.doctorklaper.com
Dr Neal Barnard	www.pcrm.org
Dr Nandita Sha	www.sharan.org
MACROVegan workshops, programmes and events	www.macrovegan.org

You will also find a full complement of videos on our TV channel at http://macrovegan.org/tv/.

Classes, Workshops and Events on offer at MACROVegan International with Bill Tara and Marlene Watson-Tara

- 4 Weeks to Vegan course
- Individual health counselling for clients with personal 21-day Vegan Plant-Based Programme
- Macrobiotic Vegan Health Coach Course (two-week intensive, graduation and certification)
- Ultimate Health Experience Mini-Break
- Plant-based nutrition lectures and workshops
- Reversing Chronic Disease with Diet and Lifestyle
- Reversing Diabetes Special Programme
- The Natural Woman – Hormonal Balanced Diet Workshop
- Tasty Tips for Kids Workshop
- Corporate programmes – The Great Escape
- Oriental Diagnosis Workshop

Our vision is to *Go Vegan* for:

Human health
The animals
The environment
World hunger
World peace

My dream is that when we have healthy humans, we will have a healthy world.

Index

adzuki beans, 240, 248. *See also* beans; Japanese
    ingredients; soups; teas and macrobiotic home
    remedies
  soup with tamari and ginger, 64
  tea, 224
adzuki bites, chocolate, 203. *See also* desserts
agar-agar, 248. *See also* Japanese ingredients
ALA. *See* alpha-linolenic acid
almond mung bean burgers with sweet
    French fries, 108–110
alpha-linolenic acid (ALA), 44
American noodle salad, 161. *See also* side dishes and
    salads
amino acids, 255
animal
  farming, 88
  proteins, 47
apple. *See also* desserts; ginger
  butter, 207
  gingered sauce, 196
arame, 248. *See also* Japanese ingredients
Asian medicine, 228
asparagus with vegan hollandaise sauce, 170. *See also*
    side dishes and salads
autumn, 169

bancha tea (kukicha), 248. *See also* Japanese
    ingredients
barley, 237. *See also* whole grains
  risotto with shiitake and sweet white miso, 124
basil and watercress pesto, 191. *See also* sauces
beans, 238, 255. *See also* Human Ecology Diet
  adzuki, 240
  amino acids, 239
  black, 239
  chickpeas, 240
  cooking, 239
  cornbread, greens and, 121–123
  enchiladas, 132–134
  fermented, 156
  kidney, 239
  lentils, 240
  pinto, 240
  soybean curd, 252
  soybeans and soy products, 240–241
  turtle, 239
  vegan bean burritos, 82
biosphere, 233
bitter, 26. *See also* tastes, five
  -tasting foods, 165
black beans, 239. *See also* beans; soups
  soup with sour cream and chives, 63
bone broth, 221
bowls, 89
  ramen bowl with fresh daikon and greens, 102
  rice and corn fusilli with broccoli and lemon cashew
      sauce, 93
  short-grain brown rice, 89
  tempeh veggie bowl with sweet peanut sauce, 97
  three bean chilli bowl, 90
  tofu brown rice bowl, 101
  vegetable seitan rice bowl, 98
  yakisoba bowl, 94
breakfast, 43
  dried berry granola, 48
  porridge with toppings, 44–46
  sweet or savoury buckwheat crepes, 52
  tips, 33
  tofu scramble on sourdough, 51
broths, 221. *See also* soups
brown rice
  short-grain, 89. *See also* bowls
  syrup, 250
buckwheat, 237. *See also* whole grains

cake, chocolate, 199. *See also* desserts
calcium, 156, 259. *See also* minerals
California rolls, 85

carbohydrate, 235–236, 246, 254–255. *See also* nutrients; whole grains

carrot cake with lemon frosting, 216. *See also* desserts

cashew cream, 196

cauliflower, herb-crusted baked, 178. *See also* side dishes and salads

cause and effect, 203

cereal grains, 104

chef's knife, 39. *See also* kitchen equipment

cherries, 46

chestnuts, 247

'chi', 25

chia seeds, 44

chickpea, 240. *See also* beans; quick bites; soups
korma, 146–148
salad sandwich, 81
and vegetable soup with peanut butter and walnut croutons, 72

China Study, The, 200

Chinese
food, 25
medicine, 54

choc chip and raisin cookies, 215. *See also* desserts

chocolate. *See also* desserts
adzuki bites, 203
cake, 199
pots, 211
sauce, 204

chopping board, 40. *See also* kitchen equipment

chowder, summer sweetcorn, 59. *See also* soups

citrus juicer, 41. *See also* kitchen equipment

coconut curry, red lentil, 106

coeliac disease, 54

colanders, 40. *See also* kitchen equipment

coleslaw, creamy, 158. *See also* side dishes and salads

cooking, 21, 54

coriander drink, parsley and, 224. *See also* teas and macrobiotic home remedies

cornbread, greens and beans, 121–123

couscous. *See also* side dishes and salads
herbed, 140
rainbow salad with tahini sauce, 162
vegetable tagine on herbed, 140–142

cravings, 34

cruciferous vegetables, 242. *See also* vegetable

cucumber wakame and peach salad with ume tangy sauce, 165. *See also* side dishes and salads

culture and eating habits, 47

cutting skills, 28

dead zones, 191

desserts, 195
black and white chocolate cake, 199
carrot cake with lemon frosting, 216
choc chip and raisin cookies, 215
chocolate adzuki bites, 203
gingered apple sauce with cashew cream and crunchy granola, 196
lemon tart, 208
mini orange chocolate pots, 211
oatmeal walnut cookies, 207
peach kanten with sweet date cream, 200
sweet cherry ice cream with chocolate sauce, 204
sweet nosh bar, 212

diet, seasonal, 48

dinner, 33

dips. *See* sauces

dressings, 29, 183. *See also* sauces

dried berry granola, 48. *See also* breakfast

dried shiitake and dried daikon, 225. *See also* teas and macrobiotic home remedies

Dr Yin's Book of Soups, 54

eating, seasonal, 188

electrolytes, 259. *See also* minerals

enchiladas, bean, 132–134

enteric nervous system, 192

fats, 189, 255–256. *See also* nutrients

fermented beans, 156

fermented foods, 156

fermented vegetables, 156, 244. *See also* vegetable

fish farms, 88

five tastes, 25
bitter, 26
examples of, 27
hot flavours, 27
pungent, 26
salty, 26
sour, 26
sweet, 26

five transformations, 25

flavourings, 196

flax seeds, 44

flour products, 254

food, 234. *See also* Human Ecology Diet; vegan diet
   additives, 212
   culture and eating habits, 47
   and environment, 231
   environmental impact of food industry, 231
   healthy, 234
   international distribution, 218
   macrobiotic, 88
   miles, 54
   nutritional impact, 88
   physical characteristics and food need, 218
   processing, 21
   replacements, 31–32
   seasonal diet, 48
   seasoning, 169
   social injustice, 232–233
   texture, 27–28
   travel, 36–37
   use of food resources, 54, 232

four weeks to vegan diet, 37–38

fructose, 246

fruit, 245–346. *See also* Human Ecology Diet

garlic press, 41. *See also* kitchen equipment

gene shift, 188

genetically modified (GM), 186

genetic disease, 182

genetic fossils, 182

ginger, 248. *See also* desserts; Japanese ingredients;
   side dishes and salads
   apple sauce with cashew cream and granola, 196
   -glazed carrots and watercress, 174
   -tamari dipping sauce, 85

global-fusion main events, 105
   almond mung bean burgers with sweet French fries,
   108–110
   barley risotto with shiitake and sweet white miso,
   124
   cornbread, greens and beans, 121–123
   jaja tofu, 128
   lasagne, 114–116
   Marlene's vegan paella, 127
   old-school macro plate, 111–113
   Portobello mushroom stroganoff, 138
   red lentil coconut curry, 106

   rice and bean enchiladas, 132–134
   roasted red pepper and chickpea korma, 146–148
   saffron-scented vegetable tagine on bed of herbed
   couscous, 140–142
   sourdough pizza, 117–120
   spaghetti with basil and watercress pesto, 152
   teriyaki black bean burgers, 135–137
   tricolour quinoa and vegetable stir-fry with teriyaki
   sauce, 149–151
   vegan shepherd's pie with shiitake gravy, 155
   vegetable and tempeh wellington with shiitake
   gravy, 143–145
   vegetable pad Thai in tamarind sauce, 131

glucose, 246, 254

gluten-free products, 54

GM. *See* genetically modified

granola, dried berry, 48. *See also* breakfast

grater, 41. *See also* kitchen equipment

greens. *See also* vegetable
   hearty, 243
   lighter, 243–244

grilled portobello and roasted red pepper sandwich, 78.
   See also quick bites

guacamole, 188. *See also* sauces

healthy
   diet, 229
   eating, short cuts to, 32–33

hearty greens, 243. *See also* vegetable

hemp seeds, 44

herb-crusted baked cauliflower, 178. *See also* side
   dishes and salads

herbed couscous, 140

Hippocrates, 219

hokkaido pumpkin, 248. *See also* Japanese ingredients

hollandaise sauce, asparagus with vegan, 170. *See also*
   side dishes and salads

hot flavours, 27. *See also* five tastes

Human Ecology Diet, 23, 182, 226. *See also* beans;
   food; Japanese ingredients; vegetable; whole
   grains
   food and environment, 231
   fruit, 245–346
   healthy diet, 229
   human health, 229–230
   macrobiotic dietary principles, 228
   mistreatment of animals, 233

modern diet, 228
nuts, 246–247
revolution, 226–227
seeds, 246–247
Standard Diet, 228
use of food resources, 232
human health, 229–230
hummus, 186–187. *See also* sauces
hydration, 260

ingredients, readily available, 34. *See also*
    Japanese ingredients
iodine, 260. *See also* minerals
iron, 259. *See also* minerals

jaja tofu, 128
Japanese ingredients, 247. *See also* Human
    Ecology Diet
  adzuki beans, 248
  agar-agar, 248
  arame, 248
  bancha tea, 248
  ginger, 248
  hokkaido pumpkin, 248
  kombu, 248–249
  kuzu, 249
  maitake mushrooms, 249
  mirin, 249
  miso, 249
  nori, 249
  pressed salad, 249
  rice syrup, 250
  sea vegetables, 250
  seitan, 250
  sesame tahini, 250
  shiitake mushrooms, 250
  shoyu, 250–251
  soba, 251
  soybeans, 251
  soy foods, 251
  soy sauce, 251
  tamari, 251
  tempeh, 251–252
  tofu, 252
  udon, 252
  umeboshi paste, 252
  umeboshi plums, 252
  umeboshi vinegar, 252
  vinegar, 252
  wakame, 252
juicing and sprouting, 244. *See also* vegetable

kale, steamed, 169. *See also* side dishes and salads
kanten, 200. *See also* desserts
karma, law of, 120
ketchup, 185. *See also* sauces
kidney beans, 239. *See also* beans
kitchen
  basics, 34–35
  tips, 29, 31
kitchen equipment, 39
  chef's knife, 39
  chopping board, 40
  citrus juicer, 41
  colanders, 40
  garlic press, 41
  grater, 41
  large pot, 42
  locking tongs, 41
  measuring cups and spoons, 40
  medium saucepan, 41
  mixing bowls, 40
  paring knife, 39
  pasta cooker, 42
  pressure cooker, 42
  salad spinner, 40
  sauté pan, 41
  slow cooker, 42
  small saucepan, 41
  stainless-steel wok, 41
  steamer, 42
  wooden spoon, 40
knife, paring, 39. *See also* kitchen equipment
kombu seaweed, 221, 248–249. *See also* Japanese
    ingredients
kukicha. *See* bancha tea
Kushi, Michio, 227
kuzu, 249. *See also* Japanese ingredients

lasagne, 114–116
law of karma, 120
lemon. *See also* bowls; desserts; sauces; side dishes
    and salads
  -infused baked tofu brown rice bowl, 101

and lime tahini sauce, 191–192

-scented arame sauté with toasted walnuts, 173

tart, 208

lentil, 240. *See also* beans; soups

coconut curry, 106

soup with sour cream, spicy brown, 71

lighter greens, 243–244. *See also* vegetable

locking tongs, 41. *See also* kitchen equipment

lunch, 33

macrobiotics, 228

dietary principles, 228

food, 88

Macrobiotic Health Coach Programme, 105

macro plate, 111–113

maitake mushrooms, 249. *See also* Japanese
ingredients

maize, 237. *See also* whole grains

Marlene's

brown rice porridge with toppings, 44–46

rich tomato sauce, 192–193. *See also* sauces

vegan paella, 127

meal balancing, 27

measuring cups and spoons, 40. *See also* kitchen
equipment

medicine, Asian, 228

Mediterranean chickpea salad sandwich, 81. *See also*
quick bites

millet, 236. *See also* bowls; whole grains

sesame-crusted tempeh veggie bowl with sweet
peanut sauce, 97

mineral broth, 221. *See also* teas and macrobiotic home
remedies

bone broth, 221

kombu seaweed, 221

recipe, 222–223

shiitake mushrooms, 222

minerals, 259. *See also* nutrients

calcium, 259

iodine, 260

iron, 259

phosphorus, 259

trace, 259

zinc, 260

mini orange chocolate pots, 211. *See also* desserts

mirin, 249. *See also* Japanese ingredients

miso, 241, 249. *See also* Japanese ingredients; soups

broth, 56

mixing bowls, 40. *See also* kitchen equipment

modern diet, 228

mushrooms, maitake, 249. *See also* Japanese
ingredients

mushroom soup with cashew cream, 74–76. *See also* soups

mushroom stroganoff, Portobello, 138

nervous system, enteric, 192

nightshade vegetables, 245. *See also* vegetable

nishime vegetable stew, 166. *See also* side dishes and
salads

non-coding DNA, 182

non-tropical fruits, 246

nori (sea laver), 249. *See also* Japanese ingredients

nutrients, 253

carbohydrate, 254–255

fat, 255–256

minerals, 259–260

protein, 255

vitamins, 256–259

water, 260

nutritional science, 227

application of Western science to, 227

deficiency diseases, 230

nuts, 246–247. *See also* Human Ecology Diet

oatmeal walnut cookies, 207. *See also* desserts

oats, 237. *See also* whole grains

quinoa nut crust, 199, 208

Ohsawa, George, 227

oil-free mayonnaise, 194. *See also* sauces

paring knife, 39. *See also* kitchen equipment

parsley and coriander drink, 224. *See also* teas and
macrobiotic home remedies

pasta cooker, 42. *See also* kitchen equipment

peach kanten with sweet date cream, 200. *See also*
desserts

peanut, 247

sauce, 97

pesticides, 156

phosphorus, 259. *See also* minerals

phytoestrogens, 186

pinto beans, 240. *See also* beans

pistou, 68

pizza, sourdough, 117–120

plant. *See also* vegan diet
  -based diet, 23–24, 227
    protein, 23

Portobello mushroom stroganoff, 138

potato wedges with ketchup, 181. *See also* side dishes
    and salads

pot, large, 42. *See also* kitchen equipment

pressed salad, 249. *See also* Japanese ingredients

pressure cooker, 42. *See also* kitchen equipment

protein, 23, 255. *See also* nutrients
    source, 47

pseudogenes, 182

pumpkin. *See also* Japanese ingredients
    hokkaido, 248
    seeds, 44

pungent, 26. *See also* tastes, five

quick bites, 77
    grilled portobello and roasted red pepper
        sandwich, 78
    Mediterranean chickpea salad sandwich, 81
    tempeh sourdough sandwich, 86
    vegan bean burritos, 82
    vegan California sushi roll with ginger-tamari dipping
        sauce, 85

quinoa, 237. *See also* whole grains
    and vegetable stir-fry with teriyaki sauce, 149–151

raisin cookies, 215. *See also* desserts

ramen bowl with fresh daikon and greens, 102. *See
    also* bowls

readily available ingredients, 34. *See also* Japanese
    ingredients

ready-made vegan foods, 116

red lentil coconut curry, 106

rice, 236. *See also* bowls; Japanese ingredients;
    whole grains
    and bean enchiladas, 132–134
    and corn with broccoli and lemon cashew
        sauce, 93
    malt, 250
    syrup, 250

risotto, barley, 124

roasted. *See also* side dishes and salads; soups
    red pepper and chickpea korma, 146–148

squash and sweet potato bisque with ume plum and
    almond cream, 60
    vegetable combo, 177

rollovers, 33–34

roots and tubers, 243. *See also* vegetable

root vegetables, 177

saffron-scented vegetable tagine on bed of herbed
    couscous, 140–142

salad. *See also* Japanese ingredients; kitchen
    equipment; side dishes and salads
    American noodle, 161
    couscous, 162
    cucumber wakame and peach salad, 165
    pressed, 249
    spinner, 40

Salmon, 88

salsa, 187–188. *See also* sauces

salty, 26. *See also* five tastes

sandwich. *See also* quick bites
    Mediterranean chickpea salad, 81
    portobello and red pepper, 78
    sourdough, 86

saucepan, medium, 41. *See also* kitchen equipment

sauces, 183
    basil and watercress pesto, 191
    guacamole, 188
    hummus, 186–187
    ketchup, 185
    lemon and lime tahini sauce, 191–192
    Marlene's tomato sauce, 192–193
    oil-free mayonnaise, 194
    salsa, 187–188
    shiitake gravy, 193
    sour cream, 185–186
    Thai dressing, 189

Sauerkraut, 244

sautéed pak choi with garlic and ginger, 113

sauté pan, 41. *See also* kitchen equipment

savoury cashew cream, 74

scrambled tofu. *See* tofu—scramble
    on sourdough

sea. *See also* Japanese ingredients; vegetable
    laver, 249
    vegetables, 245, 250

seasonal
    diet, 48

eating, 188
foods, 169
seeds, 246–247. *See also* Human Ecology Diet
seitan, 98, 250. *See also* Japanese ingredients
sesame
-crusted tempeh, 97
seeds, 44
tahini, 250. *See also* Japanese ingredients
shiitake. *See also* Japanese ingredients; teas and
macrobiotic home remedies
barley risotto with, 124
and daikon, dried, 225
mushrooms, 104, 222, 250
shiitake gravy
rich, 193. *See also* sauces
with vegetable and tempeh wellington, 143–145
short-grain brown rice, 89. *See also* bowls
shoyu (soy sauce), 250–251. *See also* Japanese
ingredients
side dishes and salads, 157
American noodle salad, 161
asparagus with vegan hollandaise sauce, 170
couscous rainbow salad with lemon and lime
tahini sauce, 162
creamy coleslaw, 158
cucumber wakame and peach salad with ume
tangy sauce, 165
ginger-glazed carrots and watercress, 174
herb-crusted baked cauliflower, 178
lemon-scented arame sauté with toasted
walnuts, 173
nishime vegetable stew, 166
potato wedges with ketchup, 181
roasted vegetable combo, 177
steamed kale with salad and sweet vinaigrette, 169
Silent Spring, The, 156
slow cooker, 42. *See also* kitchen equipment
small saucepan, 41. *See also* kitchen equipment
soba, 251. *See also* Japanese ingredients
soil and plant, 166
soup, 55, 221
adzuki bean soup with tamari and ginger, 64
beans, 121
black bean soup with sour cream and chives, 63
chickpea and vegetable soup with peanut butter
and walnut croutons, 72

creamy mushroom soup with savoury
cashew cream, 74–76
miso broth, 56
mushroom, 74–76
roasted squash and sweet potato bisque with ume
plum and almond cream, 60
spicy brown lentil soup with sour cream, 71
summer sweetcorn chowder, 59
tarragon-scented parsnip soup with sourdough
croutons, 67
umami paste organic vegetable stock, 55
white bean soup with almond pistou, 68
sour, 26. *See also* sauces; tastes, five
cream, 185–186
sourdough
pizza, 117–120
sandwich, 86. *See also* quick bites
soy
foods, 251. *See also* Japanese ingredients
sauce, 241, 250–251
soybean, 251. *See also* beans; Japanese ingredients
curd, 252
and soy products, 240–241
soy sauce. *See* shoyu
spaghetti with basil and watercress pesto, 152
sprouts, 244. *See also* vegetable
squash and potato bisque with ume plum and almond
cream, 60. *See also* soups
squashes, 242–243. *See also* vegetable
stainless-steel wok, 41. *See also* kitchen equipment
Standard Diet, 228
steamed kale with pressed salad and sweet vinaigrette,
169. *See also* side dishes and salads
steamer, 42. *See also* kitchen equipment
stockpot, 42. *See also* kitchen equipment
stroganoff, Portobello mushroom, 138
sucrose, 246
sugar, 151, 246
summer. *See also* soups
sweetcorn chowder, 59
vegetables, 165
superfoods, 234
sweet, 26. *See also* breakfast; desserts; tastes, five
almond cream, 60
buckwheat crepes, 52
cherry ice cream with chocolate sauce, 204

nosh bar, 212
    vinaigrette, 169
sweetcorn chowder, 59. *See also* soups
sweeteners, 196

tahini sauce, 51, 191–192. *See also* sauces
tamari, 251. *See also* Japanese ingredients
tarragon-scented parsnip soup with sourdough
    croutons, 67. *See also* soups
tastes, five, 25
    bitter, 26
    examples of, 27
    hot flavours, 27
    pungent, 26
    salty, 26
    sour, 26
    sweet, 26
teas and macrobiotic home remedies, 219
    adzuki bean tea, 224
    dried shiitake and daikon, 225
    mineral broth, 221–223
    parsley and coriander drink, 224
    ume sho kuzu, 223
tempeh, 241, 251–252. *See also* Japanese ingredients;
    quick bites
    sourdough sandwich, 86
teriyaki black bean burgers, 135–137
textured vegetable protein (TVP), 116
texturised soya protein (TSP), 116
Thai dressing, 189. *See also* sauces
three bean chilli bowl, 90. *See also* bowls
three sisters, 242
time saver tips, 29, 31, 32–33
tofu, 241, 252. *See also* breakfast; Japanese
    ingredients
    brown rice bowl, 101
    dish, 128
    scramble on sourdough, 51
tongs, locking, 41. *See also* kitchen equipment
trace minerals, 259. *See also* minerals
transformations, five, 25
travel, food for, 36–37
tree
    energy, 137
    nuts, 247

tricolour quinoa and vegetable stir-fry with teriyaki
    sauce, 149–151
TSP. *See* texturised soya protein
tubers, 243. *See also* vegetable
turtle beans, 239
TVP. *See* textured vegetable protein

udon, 252. *See also* Japanese ingredients
umami, 27, 27. *See also* soups
    paste organic vegetable stock, 55
umeboshi paste, 252. *See also* Japanese ingredients
umeboshi plums, 252. *See also* Japanese ingredients
umeboshi vinegar, 252. *See also* Japanese ingredients
ume plum cream, 60
ume sho kuzu, 223. *See also* teas and macrobiotic
    home remedies

vegan bean burritos, 82. *See also* quick bites
vegan California sushi roll with ginger-tamari dipping
    sauce, 85. *See also* quick bites
vegan diet, 46. *See also* plant
    four weeks to, 37–38
    macrobiotically oriented, 34
    shifting to, 24–25, 37
veganism, 15, 227
vegan shepherd's pie with shiitake gravy, 155
vegetable, 242. *See also* Human Ecology Diet; side
    dishes and salads
    cruciferous, 242
    fermented, 156, 244
    hearty greens, 243
    juicing and sprouting, 244
    lighter greens, 243–244
    nightshade, 245
    nightshade vegetables, 245
    pad Thai in tamarind sauce, 131
    roasted, 177
    root, 177
    roots and tubers, 243
    sea, 250
    sea vegetables, 245
    seitan rice bowl, 98
    squashes, 242–243
    summer, 165
    tagine on herbed couscous, 140–142

vinegar, 252. *See also* Japanese ingredients

vitamins, 256. *See also* nutrients

    fat-soluble vitamins, 257

    vitamin A, 257

    vitamin B1, 257

    vitamin B2, 257

    vitamin B3, 257

    vitamin B5, 257

    vitamin B6, 257

    vitamin B7, 257

    vitamin B9, 257

    vitamin B12, 104, 258

    vitamin C, 258–259

    vitamin D, 104, 259

    vitamin E, 259

    vitamin K, 259

    water-soluble vitamins, 257

wakame, 252. *See also* Japanese ingredients; side dishes and salads

    cucumber and peach salad with ume tangy sauce, 165

walnuts, 46

water, 260. *See also* nutrients

    footprint, 181

watercress, 174

wheat, 238. *See also* soups; whole grains

    bean with almond pistou, 68

    gluten, 250

    sensitivity, 54

whole grains, 235. *See also* Human Ecology Diet

    barley, 237

    buckwheat, 237

    carbohydrates, 235–236

    maize, 237

    merits of, 236

    millet, 236

    nutritional profile, 235

    oats, 237

    quinoa, 237

    rice, 236

    wheat, 238

wooden spoon, 40. *See also* kitchen equipment

yakisoba bowl, 94. *See also* bowls

zinc, 260. *See also* minerals

zoonoses, 120

About the Author

Marlene is a long-time vegan; activist; and lover of animals, nature and life, and is passionate about human ecology. As an eternal optimist, increasing the number of people worldwide who switch to a wholefood, plant-based diet and vegan life is her mission. Together with her husband, Bill Tara, she has created the Human Ecology Project.

As a high-profiled and dedicated health counsellor and teacher with over 40 years' experience in the health industry, Marlene's dietary advice draws from the field of macrobiotic nutrition, her studies in traditional Chinese medicine and her certification in plant-based nutrition from the T. Colin Campbell Center for Nutrition Studies. Her clients range from celebrities in the movies and arts to members of royal families. In the last 10 years she has been teaching chefs the art and skill of wholefood, plant-based cooking and nutrition. As a regular columnist for many health magazines and websites, she shares her knowledge on living healthily. Her vast experience informs a body of knowledge that she eagerly shares with the world.

Author of the internationally best-selling book *Macrobiotics for all Seasons*, Marlene teaches alongside her husband Bill Tara. They have graduates from their Macrobiotic Vegan Health Coach Programme in 27 countries. Their Ultimate Health Experience workshops have been offered in Europe, America, and Australia.

Marlene has experienced many life challenges and come out the other side with her huge gratitude for life still intact. She is not bogged down with some overriding 'theory' to prove. For her, there is no dogma. She teaches what she does and has an open mind. When she teaches, the most common sound in the room is laughter, from her and her students. Her desire to help others is as genuine as her no-nonsense approach to what works. She is a driving force for health and fitness to all who cross her path.

You will enjoy this book. The information is simple, direct and effective, and the recipes are delicious. If you follow Marlene's advice, you will be better for it. After all, that's what she guarantees.

Her favourite saying – *"If you don't look after your body, then where are you going to live?"*